MENSA®

THE MIND ASSAULT COURSE

THIS IS A CARLTON BOOK

Text and puzzle content copyright © British Mensa Limited 1998
Design and artwork copyright © Carlton Books Limited 1998

This edition published by Carlton Books Limited 1998

A CIP catalogue for this book is available from the British Library.

ISBN 1-85868-467-6

Printed and bound in Great Britain

MENSA®

THE MIND ASSAULT COURSE

Dave Chatten and Carolyn Skitt

CARLTON

ARE YOU SMART ENOUGH TO JOIN MENSA?

Solving puzzles can be a rewarding experience. The moment you discover you have unravelled the puzzle compiler's convoluted logic always brings a glow of satisfaction. But we thought you deserved something more. So Mensa are offering tangible proof of your mental powess. Solve the following fiendishly difficult puzzles and we will send you a free certificate as proof of your achievement.

1. In the space provided, place a word that can prefix the given words to form six compound words. What is the word?

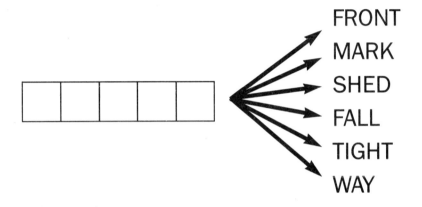

FRONT
MARK
SHED
FALL
TIGHT
WAY

2. To answer these clues you must use four letters from the word TREASURE. When completed you will be able to read a word down in the shaded column. What is the word?

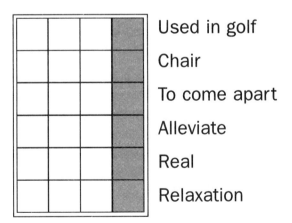

Used in golf

Chair

To come apart

Alleviate

Real

Relaxation

There, you did it! Write the answers on a postcard, together with your name and address, and send them to Mensa Puzzle Challenge, Mensa House, Freepost, Wolverhampton, WV2 1BR, England (no stamp needed). If your answers are correct, we will send you a certificate and details of how you can apply to become a Mensa member.

If you don't live in Britain and you'd like more details, you can contact:
Mensa International, 15 The Ivories, 628 Northampton Street, London N1 2NY, England
who will be happy to put you in touch with your own national Mensa.

CONTENTS

SECTION 1

ZONE 1
The Deduction Crawl 6
The Mensa Mind Assault Course Scoring System............ 21
Answers 22
Scoring System 30

ZONE 2
The Number Jump 31
Answers 60
Scoring System 67

ZONE 3
The Word Climb 68
Answers 72
Scoring System 75

ZONE 4
The Memory Tests 76
Answers 104
Scoring System 108

ZONE 5
The Spatial Logic Dodge 109
Answers 129
Scoring System 132

SECTION 2

ZONE 6
The Deduction Scramble 133
Answers 146
Scoring System 151

ZONE 7
The Number Straddle 152
Answers 178
Scoring System 187

ZONE 8
The Word Clamber 188
Answers 196
Scoring System 201

ZONE 9
More Memory Tests 202
Answers 230
Scoring System 234

ZONE 10
The Final Assault 235
Answers 254
Scoring System 256

Find your way to the end of 238 riddles requiring deductive powers worthy of Sherlock Holmes.

OBSTACLE 1   What letter appears once only in each of the first two words but not at all in the last two words?

1.	FRUITAGE	INTERPLAY	*but not in*	INTERMISSION	OSTEOPOROSIS
2.	RIPCORD	SHIELDING	*but not in*	WISTFUL	OCTAGONAL
3.	PINNACLE	COMPLAISANT	*but not in*	PINCERS	MATCHBOX
4.	IMPLICATION	MULTIFORD	*but not in*	STAMINA	WARDSHIP
5.	YEOMANLY	VALENCE	*but not in*	SPADEWORK	CARAMELIZE
6.	RAMSHACKLE	MARSHMALLOW	*but not in*	STARDUST	OCCUPATION
7.	PAWNBROKER	SINKAGE	*but not in*	WONDERFUL	SACRIFICE
8.	WINDSCREEN	IMPARTIAL	*but not in*	FICTITIOUS	CAMPAIGN
9.	INCRIMINATE	FINGERPRINT	*but not in*	ALPINE	BLUEBELL
10.	COBBLESTONE	ESTIMATE	*but not in*	GRANITE	IGNORANCE
11.	JAVELIN	ABRASIVE	*but not in*	PROMPTITUDE	RHOMBUS
12.	PICTURESQUE	IMMACULATE	*but not in*	SITUATION	HIDEOUS
13.	EDUCATIONAL	MUNDANE	*but not in*	STEADILY	RIDGEPOLE
14.	RICOCHET	GEOLOGICAL	*but not in*	OSPREY	POLYCARBON
15.	ROBUSTIOUS	SPELLBOUND	*but not in*	THUNDERCLAP	MOUTHPIECE
16.	LYRICISM	HAMSTRING	*but not in*	THISTLEDOWN	WORDLESS
17.	SORTILEGE	DISGRACED	*but not in*	PRIESTHOOD	SOPRANO
18.	GRAPEFRUIT	ACIDIFIES	*but not in*	HEADLAND	INVENTIVE
19.	SPECIFY	INVARIABLE	*but not in*	LAMINATION	STANDARD
20.	AROMATHERAPY	INSPECTION	*but not in*	MAGNIFICENT	DIRECTOR

Answers on page 22

OBSTACLE 2 Remove one letter from the first word and place it into the second word to form two new words. You must not change the order of the letters in the words and you may not use plurals. What letter needs to move?

21.	SALLOW	BAIL
22.	PITCH	SALE
23.	PRIDE	SLOE
24.	SWAMP	CLAP
25.	STILL	FACE
26.	THREE	NICE
27.	VALUE	CASE
28.	WHEAT	FAST
29.	MONTH	GLAD
30.	METAL	HOLY
31.	WRING	FIST
32.	TWINE	COME
33.	PROUD	BOND
34.	DARTED	BEACH
35.	CURVED	SHOE
36.	CREASE	BAND
37.	BUNGLE	CATER
38.	BRIDGE	FINER
39.	TWAIN	HUNT
40.	STOOP	FLAT

OBSTACLE 3 What word has a similar meaning to the first word and rhymes with the second word?

41.	CRACK	—	DRAKE
42.	BOTTOM	—	CASE
43.	RELAX	—	BEST
44.	TRUMPET	—	CUBA
45.	TRUE	—	MEAL
46.	REAR	—	LACK
47.	HOOP	—	SING
48.	CORROSION	—	MUST
49.	GRIT	—	HAND
50.	THREAD	—	GRAND

Answers on page 22

THE DEDUCTION CRAWL

OBSTACLE 4   Look at the shape below and answer the following questions on it.

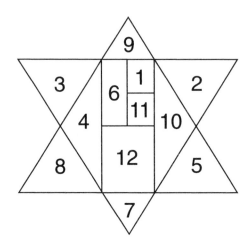

51.   How many triangles are there in the diagram?

52.   How many rectangles are there in the diagram?

53.   How many hexagons can you find?

54.   Deduct the sum of the numbers in the rectangles from the sum of the numbers in the triangles.

OBSTACLE 5   In the supermarket, the aisles are numbered one to six from the entrance. Washing powder is next to bottles and it is not the first item you see when entering the supermarket. You will see the meat aisle before the bread aisle. Tins are two aisles before bottles and meat is four aisles after fruit.

55.   What is in the last aisle (aisle six)?

56.   In which aisle can bottles be found?

57.   What is in the first aisle?

58.   In which aisle can tins be found?

Answers on page 23

OBSTACLE 6 In a car showroom, the white car is at one end of the showroom and the purple car is at the other. The red car is next to the black car and three places away from the blue car. The yellow car is next to the blue car and nearer to the purple car than to the white one. The silver car is next to the red one and the green car is five places away from the blue car. The black car is next to the green car.

59. Is the silver car or the red car nearer to the purple car?
60. Which car is three places away from the white car?
61. Which car is next to the purple car?
62. Which car is between the silver and the blue?

OBSTACLE 7 A survey has been conducted on the types of holidays people have taken over the last twelve months. Five more people had one holiday only and stayed in a self-catering accommodation than had one holiday and stayed in a hotel. Eight people had a camping holiday only and five people took all three types of holiday. Fifty-nine people had not stayed in a hotel in the last twelve months. Four times as many people went camping only as had a hotel and a camping holiday but no self-catering holiday. Of the 107 who took part in the survey a total of 35 people took a camping holiday.

63. How many people only had a hotel holiday?
64. How many people stayed in self-catering accommodation and a hotel but did not camp?
65. How many people did not stay in self-catering accommodation?
66. How many people stayed in only two of the three types of accommodation?

OBSTACLE 8 In a day at the library, 64 people borrowed books. Twice as many people borrowed a thriller only as borrowed a science fiction only. Three people borrowed a biography only and 11 people borrowed both science fiction and a thriller but not a biography. The same number borrowed a biography and a thriller but no science fiction as borrowed one of each of the three types. Twenty-one people did not borrow a thriller. One more person borrowed a science fiction book and a biography book than borrowed a biography only.

67. How many biographies were borrowed in total?
68. How many people borrowed only two of the three types?
69. How many people borrowed a thriller, a biography and a science fiction?
70. How many people borrowed a thriller only?

OBSTACLE 9 What word, which is alphabetically between the two given words, answers the clues?

71.	CURIOUS	—	CURRANT	*Twist or roll*
72.	BARRICADE	—	BARROW	*Obstruction*
73.	CABRIOLET	—	CAMPAIGN	*French town famous for cheese*
74.	CALM	—	CALVARY	*Unit of energy*
75.	DAUGHTER	—	DAY	*Beginning*
76.	DUO	—	DUPLICATE	*Deceive*
77.	EPIC	—	EPIGRAM	*Widespread disease*
78.	EPISODE	—	EPITAPH	*Letter*
79.	FAINT	—	FAITH	*Fantasy world*
80.	FALSE	—	FAME	*Waver*
81.	GOLD	—	GONDOLA	*A sport*
82.	GRAFT	—	GRAMMAR	*Cereal*
83.	HEROINE	—	HERSELF	*Fishbone pattern*
84.	HESITATE	—	HEW	*Coarse fabric*
85.	IMMATURE	—	IMMERSE	*Instant*
86.	JOG	—	JOKE	*Junction of two or more parts*
87.	KIOSK	—	KISMET	*Smoked fish*
88.	LEAF	—	LEAK	*An association*
89.	LIMBER	—	LIMIT	*Rhyme*
90.	MEDDLE	—	MEDICAL	*Intervene*

OBSTACLE 10 Match the word groups below with the given words.

91. EXTRA
92. WALL
93. VENUS
94. BEND
95. NONE

A	B	C	D	E
Mercury	Zero	Arch	Surplus	Fence
Pluto	Nil	Bow	Excess	Gate
Jupiter	Nought	Curve	Residue	Hedge
Saturn	Nothing	Concave	Remainder	Barrier

(Answers on page 24)

OBSTACLE 11   Match the word groups below with the given words.

96. WAYNE
97. FOXGLOVE
98. GARNISH
99. TOUGH
100. TWILIGHT

A	B	C	D	E
Dusk	Brando	Durable	Poppy	Trimmings
Sundown	Bogart	Strong	Crocus	Accessories
Sunset	Travolta	Sturdy	Peony	Frills
Nightfall	Swayze	Hardy	Aster	Extras

OBSTACLE 12   Match the word groups below with the given words.

101. JACKET
102. CONSTABLE
103. PUZZLE
104. CHOPIN
105. CUT

A	B	C	D	E
Ernst	Borodin	Reduce	Baffle	Cover
Rembrandt	Vivaldi	Decrease	Bewilder	Wrapper
Dali	Liszt	Lessen	Confuse	Sleeve
Picasso	Elgar	Curtail	Flummox	Envelope

Answers on pages 24 & 25

OBSTACLE 13 Match the word groups below with the given words.

106. FRANKENSTEIN
107. COUNTRY
108. ANISEED
109. FEELING
110. TRANQUIL

A	B	C	D	E
Calm	Cumin	Kingdom	Werewolf	Theory
Peaceful	Nutmeg	Realm	Demon	View
Restful	Thyme	State	Dracula	Belief
Serene	Saffron	Nation	Vampire	Opinion

OBSTACLE 14

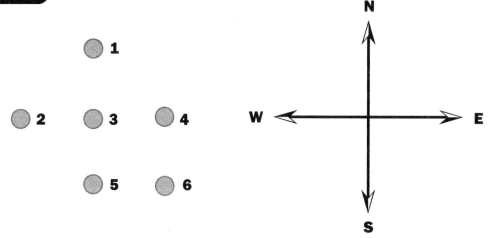

In the map above, C is south of A and south-east of D. B is south-west of F and north-west of E.

111. Which town is at point 1?
112. Which town is furthest west?
113. Which town is south-west of A?
114. Which town is north of D?
115. Which town is at point 6?

Answers on page 25

OBSTACLE 15   A certain month has five Wednesdays and the third Saturday is the 18th.

116. How many Mondays are in the month?
117. What is the date of the last Sunday of the month?
118. What is the date of the third Wednesday of the month?
119. On what day does the 23rd fall?
120. On what day does the 7th fall?

OBSTACLE 16   Three cousins have washing pegged out on the line. On each line there is a shirt, a jumper and a towel. Each has one spotted, one plain and one striped item but none of them has the same item in the same design as their cousins. Sandra's jumper is the same design as Paul's towel and Paul's jumper is the same design as Kerry's towel. Kerry's jumper is striped and Sandra's shirt is spotted.

121. Who has a spotted jumper?
122. What design is Sandra's towel?
123. Who has a striped shirt?
124. What design is Kerry's jumper?
125. What design is Paul's towel?

OBSTACLE 17   Three children, Joanna, Richard and Thomas have a pen, a crayon and a pencil-case on their desks. Each has one cat, one elephant and one rabbit design on their item but none has the same item in the same design as the others. Joanna's pencil-case is the same design as Thomas's pen and Richard's pen is the same design as Joanna's crayon. Richard has a cat on his pencil-case and Thomas has an elephant on his pen.

126. Who has a cat on their pen?
127. What design is Richard's crayon?
128. Who has a rabbit on their pencil-case?
129. What design is Thomas's pencil-case?
130. Who has a rabbit on their crayon?

THE DEDUCTION CRAWL

Answers on page 25

ZONE ①

OBSTACLE 18 The numbers on the right are formed from the numbers on the left using the same formula in each question. Find the rule and replace the question mark with a number.

131.
4 ⟶ 13
7 ⟶ 22
1 ⟶ 4
9 ⟶ ?

132.
6 ⟶ 2
13 ⟶ 16
17 ⟶ 24
8 ⟶ ?

133.
8 ⟶ 23
3 ⟶ 13
11 ⟶ 29
2 ⟶ ?

134.
6 ⟶ 10
5 ⟶ 8
17 ⟶ 32
12 ⟶ ?

135.
18 ⟶ 15
20 ⟶ 16
6 ⟶ 9
14 ⟶ ?

136.
31 ⟶ 12
15 ⟶ 4
13 ⟶ 3
41 ⟶ ?

137.
10 ⟶ 12
19 ⟶ 30
23 ⟶ 38
14 ⟶ ?

138.
9 ⟶ 85
6 ⟶ 40
13 ⟶ 173
4 ⟶ ?

139.
361 ⟶ 22
121 ⟶ 14
81 ⟶ 12
25 ⟶ ?

140.
21 ⟶ 436
15 ⟶ 220
8 ⟶ 59
3 ⟶ ?

141.
5 ⟶ 65
2 ⟶ 50
14 ⟶ 110
8 ⟶ ?

142.
15 ⟶ 16
34 ⟶ 92
13 ⟶ 8
20 ⟶ ?

143.
5 ⟶ 38
12 ⟶ 80
23 ⟶ 146
9 ⟶ ?

144.
7 ⟶ 15
16 ⟶ 51
4 ⟶ 3
21 ⟶ ?

Answers on page 26

145. 36 ⟶ 12
56 ⟶ 17
12 ⟶ 6
40 ⟶ ?

146. 145 ⟶ 26
60 ⟶ 9
225 ⟶ 42
110 ⟶ ?

147. 25 ⟶ 72
31 ⟶ 108
16 ⟶ 18
19 ⟶ ?

148. 8 ⟶ 99
11 ⟶ 126
26 ⟶ 261
15 ⟶ ?

149. 8 ⟶ 100
13 ⟶ 225
31 ⟶ 1089
17 ⟶ ?

150. 29 ⟶ 5
260 ⟶ 16
13 ⟶ 3
40 ⟶ ?

OBSTACLE 19

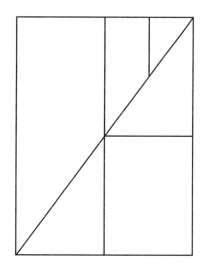

151. How many different sections are there in the drawing?
152. How many triangles are in the drawing?
153. How many rectangles are in the drawing?
154. How many right angles are in the drawing?
155. If the vertical middle line is central, how many similar triangles are there?

Answers on page 26

THE DEDUCTION CRAWL

	MONKEYS	LLAMAS	LIONS
WILDLIFE PARK A	42	25	16
WILDLIFE PARK B	35	21	14
WILDLIFE PARK C	48	32	10

156. Which park has twice as many monkeys as Park B has llamas?

157. Which park has one quarter of the total lions?

158. At which park does the sum of the llamas and lions total the number of monkeys?

159. Which park has three times as many monkeys as Park A has lions?

160. Which park has twice as many llamas as one of the parks has lions?

OBSTACLE 21   Can you find a word that begins with the letter "A", which is opposite in meaning to the given word?

161. VANISH

162. BELOW

163. FORFEIT

164. CONVICT

165. SWEETNESS

166. PRESENT

167. IMAGINARY

168. EXTEND

169. OPPRESSIVE

170. IMMATURE

OBSTACLE 22   Can you find a word beginning with the letter "H", which is opposite in meaning to the following?

171. EXCEPTIONAL

172. SERIOUS

173. DIGNIFY

174. FRIENDLY

175. DOCILE

176. FREE

177. DESPAIRING

178. PROSPERITY

179. VILLAIN

180. SATISFIED

OBSTACLE 23   In a picture showing a winter scene there are people wearing hats, scarves and gloves. The same number can be seen wearing a hat only as wearing a scarf and gloves only. There are only four people who are not wearing a hat. Five people are wearing a hat and a scarf but no gloves. Twice as many people are wearing a hat only as a scarf only. Eight people are not wearing gloves and seven are not wearing a scarf. One more person can be seen wearing all three than wearing a hat only.

181.   How many people are wearing hat, scarf and gloves?
182.   How many people are wearing gloves only?
183.   How many people are wearing a scarf only?
184.   How many people are wearing a hat and gloves but no scarf?
185.   How many people are wearing gloves?
186.   How many people can be seen in the picture?

OBSTACLE 24   In break-time at a shop children can buy chips, candy and soda. Two more children buy candy only than chips only. Thirty-seven children do not buy any candy at all. Two more children buy both chips and soda but no candy than candy only. A total of 60 children buy soda, but only nine of them have soda only. Twelve children buy chips only. One more child buys candy only than candy and soda only, and three more buy both chips and candy but no soda than buy chips and soda but no candy.

187.   How many children buy all three items?
188.   How many children buy chips and candy but no soda?
189.   How many children buy chips and soda but no candy?
190.   How many children visit the shop?
191.   How many children do not have chips?
192.   How many children have candy only?

OBSTACLE 25   Sausage, fries and beans are being served to 22 people. The same number have sausage and fries only as sausage and beans only. Only seven do not have fries. The same number have fries and beans only as fries only. Twice as many have beans and sausage but no fries as have sausage only. One person has beans only and one more person has sausage, fries and beans than sausage and fries only.

193. How many people have sausage, fries and beans?
194. How many people have sausage only?
195. How many people do not have beans?
196. How many people do not have sausage?
197. How many people have fries and beans but no sausage?
198. How many people have sausage and fries only?

OBSTACLE 26   On sports day the fastest runners are taking part in the sprint, the hurdles and the relay. One more person takes part in the hurdles only than the sprint only. The same number take part in the sprint and the hurdles as take part in the relay and the hurdles. Eleven of the athletes taking some part in these three races do not do the relay. Five people take part in the sprint and the relay and three enter all three races. There are four teams of four runners in the relay. One more person is running in both the relay and the sprint than in the hurdles only.

199. How many people are taking some part in any of the three races?
200. How many people are taking part in the relay only?
201. How many people do not take part in the hurdles?
202. How many people do not take part in the sprint?
203. How many people take part in both the hurdles and relay but not the sprint?
204. How many people take part in two races only?

OBSTACLE 27   A survey has been carried out on TV viewing. The survey shows the percentages of people who watch soaps, documentaries and movies. 26% of people watch all three. 39% of people do not watch documentaries. The percentage of people watching soaps only plus the percentage of people watching movies only is the same as the number who watch both movies and documentaries. 27% of people do not watch movies, 14% watch both soaps and documentaries and 3% watch documentaries only.

205.   What percentage of people watch both soaps and movies but no documentaries?

206.   What percentage watch soaps only?

207.   What percentage watch movies and documentaries but not soaps?

208.   What percentage watch movies only?

209.   What percentage watch only two out of the three types of show?

210.   What percentage watch only one type of show?

OBSTACLE 28   At a pick-your-own fruit farm, twice as many people are picking raspberries only as plums only. Three more people pick strawberries, raspberries and plums as pick plums only. Four more people pick strawberries only as pick both raspberries and strawberries but not plums. 50 people do not pick strawberries. Eleven people pick both plums and raspberries but not strawberries. A total of 60 people pick plums. If the total number of fruit pickers is 100, can you answer the questions below?

211.   How many people pick raspberries?

212.   How many people pick all three?

213.   How many people pick raspberries only?

214.   How many people pick both plums and strawberries but no raspberries?

215.   How many people pick strawberries only?

216.   How many people pick only two of the three fruits?

Answers on page 28

OBSTACLE 29 At a college teaching crafts, sciences and humanities, the new intake of students can study a maximum of two of the three subjects. One more student is studying a craft and a humanities than a craft only. Two more are studying both a science and a humanities than are studying both a craft and a science. Half as many are studying both a craft and a humanities as are studying both a craft and a science. 21 students are not doing a craft subject. Three students are studying a humanities subject only and six are studying a science only.

217. How many students are not studying a science?
218. How many students are studying both a science and humanities?
219. How many students are studying two subjects?
220. How many students are studying only one subject?
221. How many students are not doing a humanities subject?
222. How many students are studying a craft only?

OBSTACLE 30 At a kennel there are Labradors, Alsatians and Greyhounds and also crosses of these breeds. There are two more true Labradors than true Alsatians. Six dogs are Alsatian and Labrador crosses. Ten dogs have no Labrador or Alsatian in them. Only one dog is a mixture of all three breeds. There are twice as many Labrador and Alsatian crosses than Labrador and Greyhound crosses. There is one more Alsatian and Greyhound cross than Labrador and Greyhound cross. Twenty-two dogs do not have any Alsatian in them. There are 40 dogs in total in the kennels.

223. How many true Labradors are there?
224. How many true Alsatians are there?
225. How many true Greyhounds are there?
226. How many Labrador and Greyhound crosses are there?
227. How many Alsatian and Greyhound crosses are there?
228. How many dogs do not have any Labrador in them?

OBSTACLE 31 What word has a similar meaning to the first word and rhymes with the second word?

229.	FRUIT	—	GATE	230.	PRICE	—	LOST
231.	STOPPER	—	FORK	232.	LEAN	—	SHIN
233.	SPHERE	—	WALL	234.	LINK	—	FOND
235.	INSTRUMENT	—	CARP	236.	FACE	—	TILE
237.	GROOVE	—	BLOT	238.	LOAN	—	SEND

Answers on page 29

The Mensa Mind Assault Course

Compare your scores in each section against the scoring charts. If you are under 16 years old you must add the bonus points for your age grouping.

The aim is to find out how intelligent you are and the most intelligent are given promotions on the completion of each Zone. Score 1 point for each correct answer.

The list of ratings or ranks for the Mind Obstacle Course are given below. You can get promoted or demoted as you advance through the zones. Only the very highest intellects will make it to Five Star Generals.

Structure of Ranks in the Mensa Mind Army

Private "Third Class"
Private "Second Class"
Private "First Class"
Acting Corporal
Corporal
Sergeant   –   **Average Intelligence Level**
Master Sergeant
Second Lieutenant
Lieutenant
Captain
Major   –   **High Intelligence Level**
Lieutenant Colonel
Colonel
General   (One Star)   –   **Very High Intelligence Level**
               (Two Star)
               (Three Star)
               (Four Star)
               (Five Star)

If you have scored Major or higher it is recommended that you contact your National Mensa for their IQ assessment test (see page 4 for details).

ZONE ①

ANSWERS

OBSTACLE 1

1. A.	2. D.	3. L.	4. O.	5. N.
6. H.	7. K.	8. R.	9. T.	10. S.
11. V.	12. C.	13. U.	14. I.	15. B.
16. M.	17. G.	18. F.	19. E.	20. P.

OBSTACLE 2

21. S, to make Allow, Basil.	22. C, to make Pith, Scale.
23. P, to make Ride, Slope.	24. M, to make Swap, Clamp.
25. T, to make Sill, Facet.	26. H, to make Tree, Niche.
	Or R, to make Thee, Nicer.
27. U, to make Vale, Cause.	28. E, to make What, Feast.
29. N, to make Moth, Gland.	30. T, to make Meal, Hotly.
31. R, to make Wing, First.	32. T, to make Wine, Comet.
33. U, to make Prod, Bound.	34. R, to make Dated, Breach.
35. V, to make Cured, Shove	36. R, to make Cease, Brand.
37. N, to make Bugle, Canter.	38. G, to make Bride, Finger.
39. A, to make Twin, Haunt.	40. O, to make Stop, Float.

OBSTACLE 3

41. Break.	42. Base.
43. Rest.	44. Tuba.
45. Real.	46. Back.
47. Ring.	48. Rust.
49. Sand.	50. Strand.

OBSTACLE 4

51. 14.
52. 7.
53. 2 (using segment numbers 1, 6, 7, 9, 11, 12 and 1, 4, 6, 10, 12).
54. 18.

OBSTACLE 5

The aisle order is: 1. fruit, 2. tins, 3. washing powder, 4. bottles, 5. meat, 6. bread.

55. Bread.
56. Four.
57. Fruit.
58. Two.

OBSTACLE 6

From one end or the other, the order is: white, green, black, red, silver, yellow, blue, purple.

59. Silver.
60. Red.
61. Blue.
62. Yellow.

OBSTACLE 7

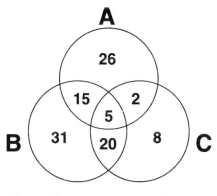

A = Hotel, **B** = Self-Catering, **C** = Camping.

63. 26. **64.** 15. **65.** 36. **66.** 37.

ZONE ①

OBSTACLE 8

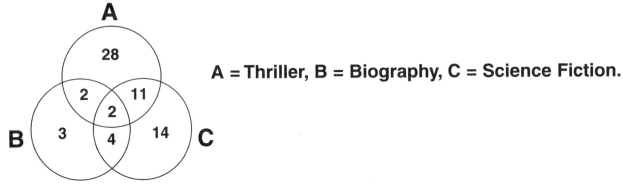

A = Thriller, B = Biography, C = Science Fiction.

67. 11.   **68.** 17.   **69.** 2.   **70.** 28.

OBSTACLE 9

71.	Curl.	**72.**	Barrier.
73.	Camembert.	**74.**	Calorie.
75.	Dawn.	**76.**	Dupe.
77.	Epidemic.	**78.**	Epistle.
79.	Fairyland.	**80.**	Falter.
81.	Golf.	**82.**	Grain.
83.	Herringbone.	**84.**	Hessian.
85.	Immediate.	**86.**	Joint.
87.	Kipper.	**88.**	League.
89.	Limerick.	**90.**	Mediate.

OBSTACLE 10

91. D.   **92.** E.   **93.** A.   **94.** C.   **95.** B.

OBSTACLE 11

96. B.   **97.** D.   **98.** E.   **99.** C.   **100.** A.

Answers

OBSTACLE 12

101. E.   **102.** A.   **103.** D.   **104.** B.   **105.** C.

OBSTACLE 13

106. D.   **107.** C.   **108.** B.   **109.** E.   **110.** A.

OBSTACLE 14

111. F.   **112.** B.   **113.** E.   **114.** F.   **115.** C.

OBSTACLE 15

116. Four.   **117.** 26th.
118. 15th.   **119.** Thursday.
120. Tuesday.

OBSTACLE 16
Kerry has a striped jumper, plain shirt and spotted towel; Paul has a spotted jumper, striped shirt and plain towel; Sandra has a plain jumper, spotted shirt and striped towel.

121. Paul.   **122.** Striped.
123. Paul.   **124.** Striped.
125. Plain.

OBSTACLE 17
Joanna has a cat on her pen, a rabbit on her crayon and an elephant on her pencil-case; Richard has a rabbit on his pen, an elephant on his crayon and a cat on his pencil-case; Thomas has an elephant on his pen, a cat on his crayon and a rabbit on his pencil-case.

126. Joanna.   **127.** Elephant.
128. Thomas.   **129.** Rabbit.
130. Joanna.

Answers

ZONE ①

OBSTACLE 18

131.	28. (x 3) + 1.	**132.**	6. (– 5) x 2.
133.	11. (x 2) + 7.	**134.**	22. (x 2) – 2.
135.	13. (÷ 2) + 6.	**136.**	17. (– 7) ÷ 2.
137.	20. (– 4) x 2.	**138.**	20. (squared) + 4.
139.	8. (√) + 3.	**140.**	4. (squared) – 5.
141.	80. (+ 8) x 5.	**142.**	36. (– 11) x 4.
143.	62. (x 6) + 8.	**144.**	71. (x 4) – 13.
145.	13. (÷ 4) + 3.	**146.**	19. (÷ 5) – 3.
147.	36. (– 13) x 6.	**148.**	162. (+ 3) x 9.
149.	361. + 2, then squared.	**150.**	6. – 4, then √.

OBSTACLE 19

151. 6.　　**152.** 6.　　**153.** 5.　　**154.** 14.　　**155.** 4.

OBSTACLE 20

156. A.　　**157.** C.　　**158.** B.　　**159.** C.　　**160.** C.

OBSTACLE 21

161.	Appear.	**162.**	Above.
163.	Acquire.	**164.**	Acquit.
165.	Acerbity.	**166.**	Absent.
167.	Actual.	**168.**	Abbreviate.
169.	Airy.	**170.**	Adult.

OBSTACLE 22

171.	Humdrum.	**172.**	Humorous.
173.	Humiliate.	**174.**	Hostile.
175.	Headstrong.	**176.**	Hold.
177.	Hopeful.	**178.**	Hardship.
179.	Hero.	**180.**	Hungry.

Answers

OBSTACLE 23

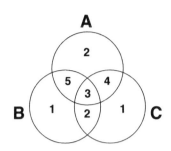

A = Hat, B = Scarf, C = Gloves.

181. 3.	**182.** 1.	**183.** 1.
184. 4.	**185.** 10.	**186.** 18.

OBSTACLE 24

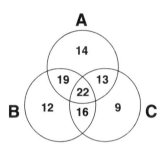

A = Candy, B = Chips, C = Soda.

187. 22.	**188.** 19.	**189.** 16.
190. 105.	**191.** 36.	**192.** 14.

OBSTACLE 25

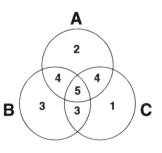

A = Sausage, B = Fries, C = Beans.

193. 5.	**194.** 2.	**195.** 9.
196. 7.	**197.** 3.	**198.** 4.

Answers

ZONE ①

OBSTACLE 26

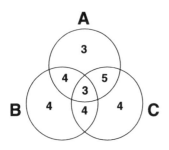

A = Sprint, B = Hurdles, C = Relay.

199. 27. **200.** 4. **201.** 12.
202. 12. **203.** 4. **204.** 13.

OBSTACLE 27

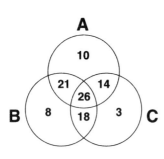

A = Soaps, B = Movies, C = Documentaries.

205. 21. **206.** 10. **207.** 18.
208. 8. **209.** 53. **210.** 21.

OBSTACLE 28

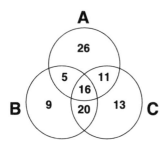

A = Raspberries, B = Strawberries, C = Plums.

211. 58. **212.** 16. **213.** 26.
214. 20. **215.** 9. **216.** 36.

Answers

OBSTACLE 29

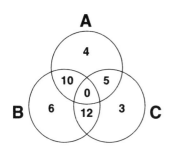

A = Craft, B = Science, C = Humanities.

217. 12.	**218.** 12.	**219.** 27.
220. 13.	**221.** 20.	**222.** 4.

OBSTACLE 30

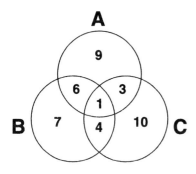

A = Labrador, B = Alsatian, C = Greyhound.

223. 9.	**224.** 7.	**225.** 10.
226. 3.	**227.** 4.	**228.** 21.

OBSTACLE 31

229. Date.
230. Cost.
231. Cork.
232. Thin.
233. Ball.
234. Bond.
235. Harp.
236. Dial.
237. Slot.
238. Lend.

THE DEDUCTION CRAWL

Answers

ZONE ①

SCORING SYSTEM

How did you fare?

Promotion Criteria (See page 21):

Under 120	*"Back to Boot Camp"*. Private "Third Class".
121 - 150	*"Pass Boot Camp"*. Private "Second Class".
151 - 190	Private "First Class".
191 - 220	Acting Corporal.
221+	Corporal.

If you are under 16 don't forget to add your Age Bonus Points

AGE IN YEARS	10	10.5	11	11.5	12	12.5	13	13.5	14	14.5	15	15.5
BONUS POINTS	40	35	30	25	20	18	16	18	12	10	8	4

A spring in the step and a clear head will be required to leap over this set of 152 mathematical hurdles.

OBSTACLE 1 Six children have invented a card game and scoring system. It uses the cards up to 10, at face value, with aces scoring 1. In each round, the value of the card dealt is added to that child's score. Diamonds are worth double the face value. If two or more children are dealt cards with the same face value in one round, they lose the value of the that card instead of gaining it(diamonds still doubled). They are each dealt six cards face up as shown below:

Player	Card 1	Card 2	Card 3	Card 4	Card 5	Card 6
1	6 ♥	3 ♠	ACE ♦	9 ♣	10 ♥	4 ♠
2	10 ♠	ACE ♠	7 ♥	6 ♦	5 ♠	8 ♣
3	7 ♦	8 ♥	4 ♣	3 ♥	ACE ♣	5 ♣
4	4 ♥	9 ♦	7 ♠	5 ♦	10 ♣	3 ♦
5	8 ♠	5 ♥	6 ♠	9 ♠	2 ♠	4 ♦
6	3 ♣	2 ♣	9 ♥	7 ♣	10 ♦	8 ♦

When the scores are added up, which player:

1. Came third?
2. Won?
3. Came last?
4. Was winning after the fourth cards had been dealt?
5. Had even scores?
6. Had a score divisible by 3?
7. What was the second highest score?
8. What was the sum of all of the scores?

Answers on page 60

ZONE ②

OBSTACLE 2   A farmer keeps only four types of animals. He has a total of 560 animals. If he had 10 sheep less he would have twice as many sheep as he has cows. If he had 10 cows less he would have three cows for every pig, and he has two and one half pigs to every horse.

9. How many pigs does he have?

10. How many horses does he have?

11. If he swaps 75% of his cows for 7 sheep per cow, how many animals will he have in total?

12. How many sheep will he have after the swap?

OBSTACLE 3

13. What number should replace the symbols in this grid if only the numbers 1 to 7 can be used?

❏	❏	△	○	★	14
★	○	△	○	◉	19
❏	○	◉	○	○	23
○	★	◉	★	★	9
○	○	★	■	○	23
16	15	19	18	20	?

OBSTACLE 4   What numbers should replace the question marks in the series below?

14.	7	9	16	25	41	**?**		
15.	4	14	34	74	**?**			
16.	2	3	5	5	9	7	14	**?**	**?**
17.	6	9	15	27	**?**			
18.	11	7	−1	−17	**?**			
19.	8	15	26	43	**?**			
20.	3.5	4	7	14	49	**?**		

Answers on Pages 60 & 61

OBSTACLE 5   What numbers are missing from these number grids?

21.

A	B	C	D	E
7	5	3	4	8
9	8	8	8	8
6	4	9	3	5
8	3	6	?	9

22.

A	B	C	D	E
7	8	7	9	7
5	5	8	5	9
6	3	7	3	9
4	4	8	6	?

23.

A	B	C	D	E
3	5	4	6	3
4	8	5	9	7
6	1	5	4	6
2	2	?	1	4

THE NUMBER JUMP

Answers on page 61

THE NUMBER JUMP

OBSTACLE 6 What numbers should replace the question marks?

24.

 = 174    = 993

= ?

25.

 = 18

X = 28

 X = ?

26.

27.

Answers on page 61

OBSTACLE 7 The numbers in box 1 move clockwise to the positions shown in box 2. In which positions should the missing numbers appear?

28.

1

2	6	7
11		1
10	3	5

2

	10	
7		2
	11	

29.

1

22	15	34
12		14
23	21	19

2

14		12
19		23

30.

1

3	5	8
1		6
17	7	9

2

	1	
5		8
	7	

Answers on pages 61 & 62

OBSTACLE 8 What numbers should replace the question marks?

31.

7534	41	3
9624	72	5
5816	42	?

32.

3569	2307	104
7678	5426	380
9925	4185	?

33.

6225	1210	20
7946	6324	188
3483	1224	?

THE NUMBER JUMP

Answers on page 62

ZONE ②

OBSTACLE 9   Divide these two grids into four identical shapes. The sum of the numbers contained within each of the shapes must give the totals shown.

34.   Totals **120**

8	7	6	8	7	12	9	1
7	12	7	6	4	3	2	14
8	9	7	8	5	7	11	1
8	8	10	7	6	16	10	1
4	9	13	4	12	2	15	6
8	5	2	2	4	9	8	15
6	9	8	14	14	8	2	1
9	6	10	5	12	1	5	17

35.   Totals **134**

5	7	8	15	4	7	5	6
11	6	9	8	16	12	10	10
7	12	10	12	3	11	6	8
6	7	2	5	7	7	15	10
12	15	10	8	5	12	8	7
6	7	11	13	9	6	9	6
9	8	10	6	8	8	1	2
3	6	4	10	10	10	15	15

Answers on page 62

OBSTACLE 10   The values of grids A and B are given. What is the value of the grid C?

36.

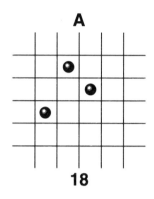 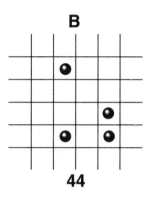 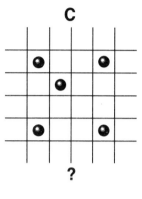

     A   B   C

     18   44   ?

37.

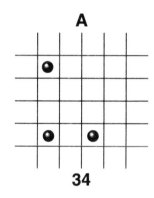 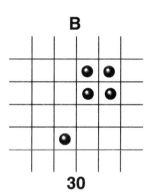 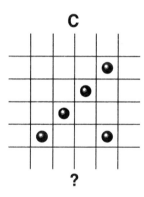

     A   B   C

     34   30   ?

A triangle denotes the grid value and a circle denotes twice the grid value. The values of grids A and B are given. What is the value of the grid C?

38.

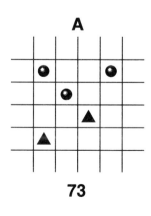 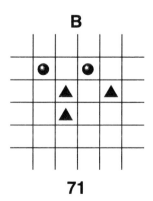 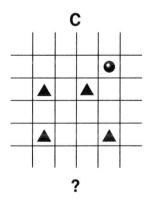

     A   B   C

     73   71   ?

THE NUMBER JUMP

Answers on page 63

OBSTACLE 11 Can you calculate the numbers missing in the figures below? Each number is used once only and is not reversed.

39.

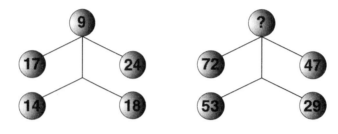

40.

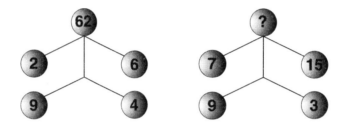

41.

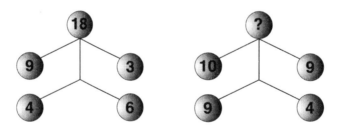

42.

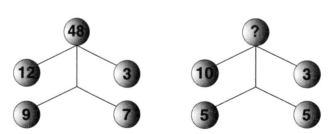

40

Answers on page 63

43.

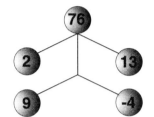 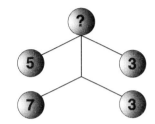

44.

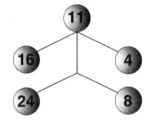 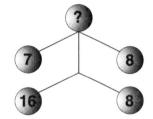

45.

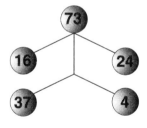 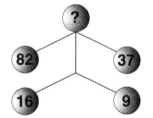

46.

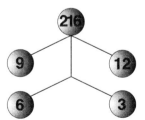 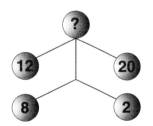

THE NUMBER JUMP

Answers on page 63

ZONE ②

47.

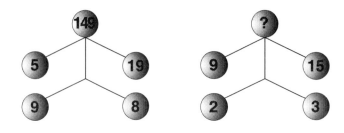

48.

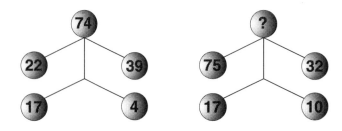

OBSTACLE 12 Starting at the top number, find a route that goes down one level each time until you reach the bottom number.

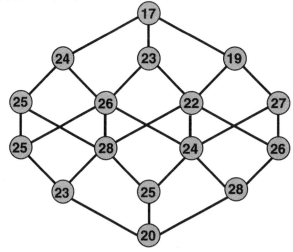

49. Can you find a route where the sum of the numbers is 130?

50. Can you find two separate routes that give a total of 131?

51. What is the highest possible score and what route/s do you follow?

52. What is the lowest possible score and what route/s do you follow?

53. How many ways are there to score 136 and what route/s do you follow?

42

(**Answers on page 63**)

OBSTACLE 13 Starting at the top number, find a route that goes down one level each time until you reach the bottom number.

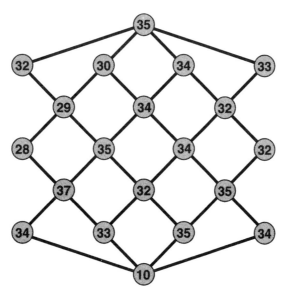

54. Can you find a route where the sum of the numbers is 216?
55. Can you find two separate routes that give a total of 204?
56. What is the highest possible score and what route/s do you follow?
57. What is the lowest possible score and what route/s do you follow?
58. How many ways are there to score 211 and what route/s do you follow?

OBSTACLE 14 What is the value of the last string in each of these problems if the first three strings have values as given? Black, white and shaded circles have different values.

59.

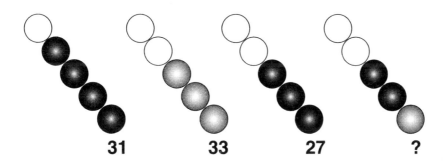

| 31 | 33 | 27 | ? |

Answers on page 64

43

THE NUMBER JUMP

60.

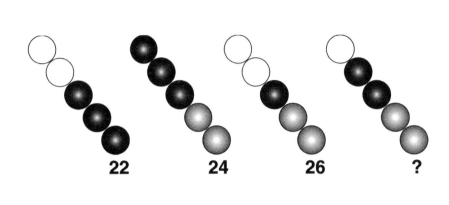

22   24   26   ?

61.

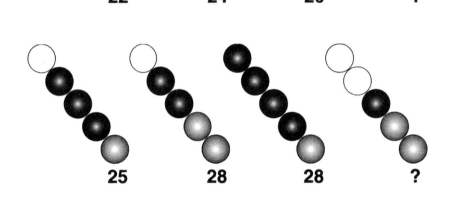

25   28   28   ?

62.

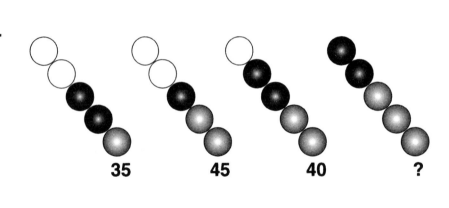

35   45   40   ?

63.

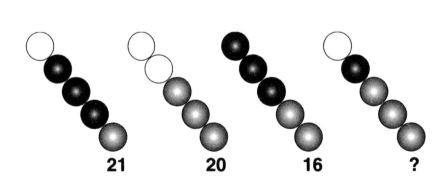

21   20   16   ?

44

Answers on page 64

64.

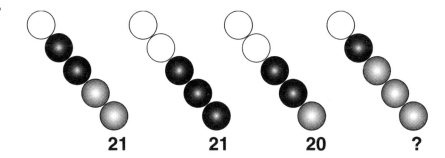

21   21   20   ?

65.

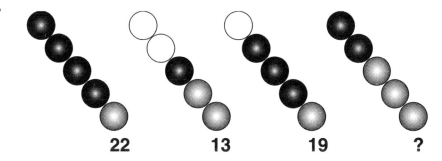

22   13   19   ?

66.

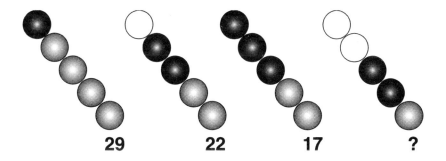

29   22   17   ?

67.

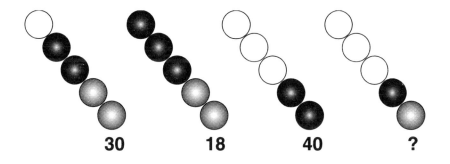

30   18   40   ?

Answers on page 64

THE NUMBER JUMP

THE NUMBER JUMP

68.

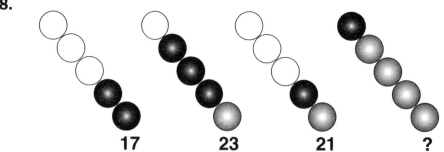

17   23   21   ?

OBSTACLE 15 The numbers on the grids below are found by giving the value of any symbol that is adjacent horizontally, vertically or diagonally. The numbers are then halved in adjacent boxes. If there is more than one value that can go in a box, then they are added together. See examples below.

	A	B	C	D	E	F
1	2	2	2	2	0	0
2	4	4	4	2	0	0
3	4	×	4	2	0	0
4	4	4	4	2	0	0
5	2	2	2	2	0	0
6	0	0	0	0	0	0

+

	A	B	C	D	E	F
1	0	5	5	5	5	5
2	0	5	10	10	10	5
3	0	5	10	△	10	5
4	0	5	10	10	10	5
5	0	5	5	5	5	5
6	0	0	0	0	0	0

=

	A	B	C	D	E	F
1	2	7	7	7	5	5
2	4	9	14	12	10	5
3	4	×	14	△	10	5
4	4	9	14	12	10	5
5	2	7	7	7	5	5
6	0	0	0	0	0	0

If   ✕ = 4   **&**   △ = 10

The grid value would look like the example

$$C1 = (D3 \times \tfrac{1}{2}) + (B3 \times \tfrac{1}{2}) = 7$$
$$A5 = B3 \times \tfrac{1}{2} = 2$$
$$D4 = D3 + (B3 \times \tfrac{1}{2}) = 12$$

From the information in the grid below, complete the grid and answer the questions that follow:

	A	B	C	D	E	F
1						
2	32	●			⊤	16
3			□			
4		⊤			□	
5					●	
6			22			28

69. What is the value of square D1?

70. What is the value of square A3?

71. What is the value of square F3?

72. What square has the highest value?

73. What is the value of □?

74. What is the value of the lowest square?

75. What are the values of the symbols ● and ⊤?

76. Which 3 squares have a value of 32?

Now try this more difficult grid using the same rules:

	A	B	C	D	E	F
1	△					24
2			★	△	△	
3	37		⊗			
4					⊗	
5		⊗				
6				△		20

77. What are the values of the three symbols?

78. What is the value of the highest square?

79. What is the value of square C4?

80. What is the value of the lowest square?

81. What is the value of square E3?

82. How many squares have a value of 64?

Answers on page 64

THE NUMBER JUMP

OBSTACLE 16 Start at the top-left circle and move clockwise. Calculate the number that replaces the question marks in the following:

83.

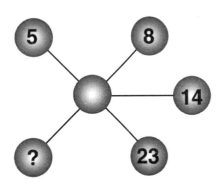

84.

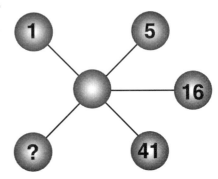

85.

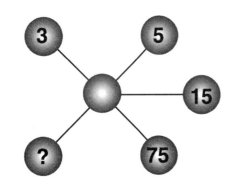

86.

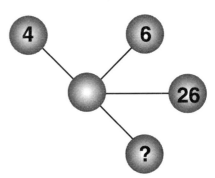

87.

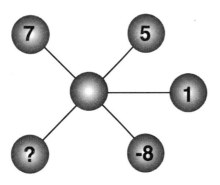

88.

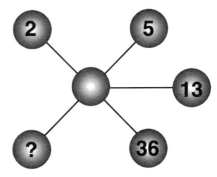

48

Answers on page 65

89.

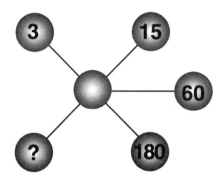

90.

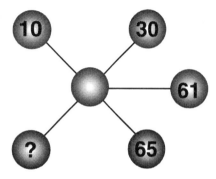

91.

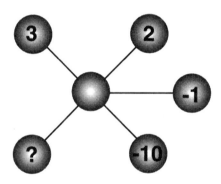

92.

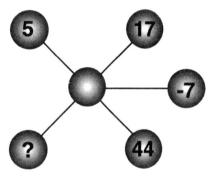

93.

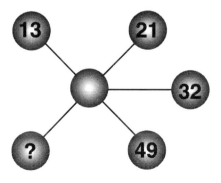

94.

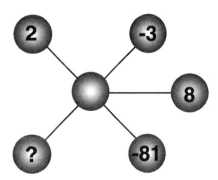

Answers on page 65

THE NUMBER JUMP

95.

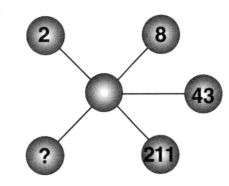

96.

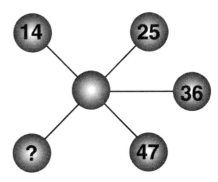

97.

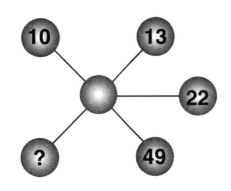

98.

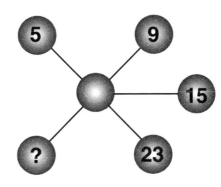

99.

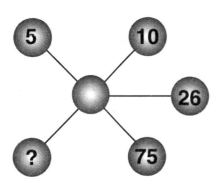

100.

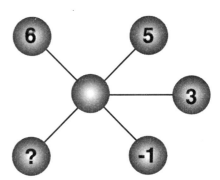

101.

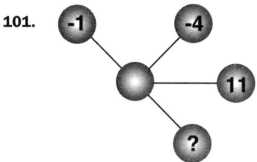

102.

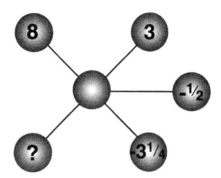

OBSTACLE 17 The number in the middle knot of the following bow ties is reached by using all of the outer numbers only once. You cannot reverse the numbers to obtain the answers. Which numbers should replace the question marks?

103.

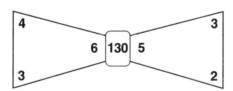

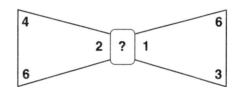

104.

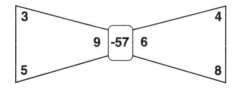

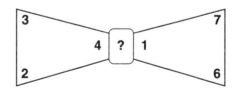

105.

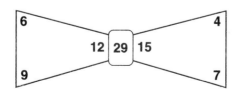

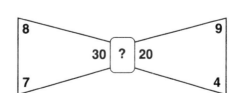

Answers on page 65

THE NUMBER JUMP

106.

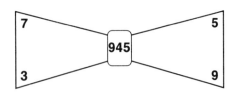
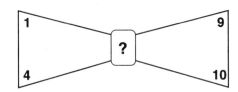

107.

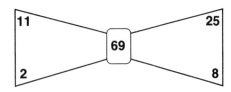
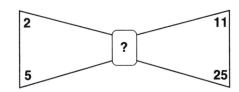

108.

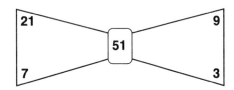
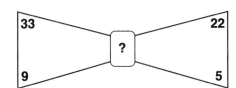

OBSTACLE 18 In the grid below, the intersections have a value equal to the sum of their four touching numbers.

	A	B	C	D	E	F	G	
1	30	19	28	26	25	36	16	29
2	24	20	26	23	24	23	24	22
3	26	29	27	20	25	29	27	23
4	20	23	28	32	29	30	24	22
5	30	28	27	22	30	26	27	29
6	20	28	23	28	32	29	31	26
7	25	27	25	27	30	26	24	19
	26	26	29	23	24	28	24	28

Can you answer the following:

109. What are the grid references for the three intersection points with a value of 100?

110. Which intersection point/s has a value of 92?

111. How many intersections have a value of less than 100?

112. Which intersection has the highest value?

113. Which intersection has the lowest value?

114. Which intersection/s has a value of 115?

115. How many intersections have a value of 105 and which are they?

116. How many intersections have a value of 111 and which are they?

OBSTACLE 19 Can you find the missing values on the roofs of the following houses? Each of the numbers on the windows and door must be used only once and no number can be reversed.

117.

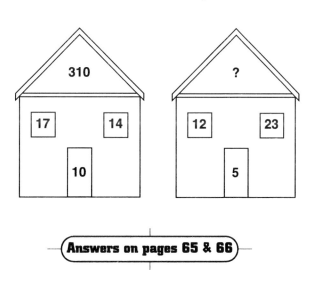

THE NUMBER JUMP

118.

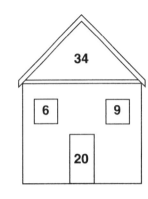 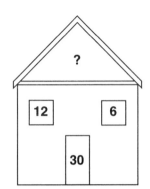

119.

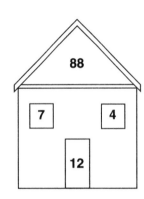 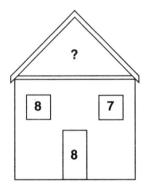

120.

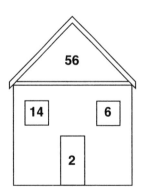 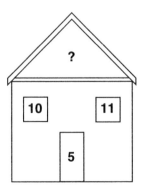

121.

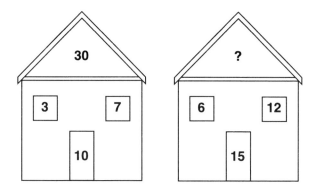

122.

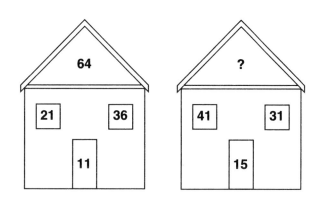

OBSTACLE 20

123. If two-thirds of a number is three-quarters of $42\frac{2}{3}$, what is that number?

124. If half the square root of a number is one-fifth of 20, what is that number?

125. If half of a positive number is squared and is then halved again, and it is equal to the original number, what is that number?

126. If a quarter of a number is equal to the cube root of 512, what is that number?

127. If 50% of a positive number is equal to twice the square root of that number, what is that number?

Answers on page 66

THE NUMBER JUMP

THE NUMBER JUMP

128. If twice a number is squared and it is equal to one-half of 50, what is that number?

129. If 3 is subtracted from a number and the remainder is squared, it is 45 less than the original number squared. What was that number?

130. If 10 times a number is the square root of another number that is 1000 times the number, what is that number?

131. If 26 times a number is 1/26 of 4 x 50, what is that number?

132. If 40 times a number is half of 7 x 8 x 10, what is that number?

133. How can 0.18 + 0.19 relate to a lion?

134. What two whole numbers squared add up to 50?

135. A shopkeeper has a full box of nails that contains 8200 nails. He also has 250 packets of 12 nails, 200 packets of 24 nails, 180 packets of 10 nails and 372 assorted loose nails. How many more nails can he put in the box?

136. Simon had a bag of candy. When he tried to divide them into three piles he had one left over. The same happened when he tried to divide them into four, five and six piles. But when he split them into seven piles he had none left over. How many candies did he start with?

137. A number contains eight digits, two each of 1, 2, 3 and 4. The 1s are separated by one digit, the 2s by two digits, the 3s by three digits and the 4s by four digits. Reconstruct the number to give an answer that can be read in either direction.

138. A man playing roulette had a winning streak. Each time he won he gambled half of his total money at odds that would double his stake if he won. He started with $64 and after eight spins he had $546.75. What was his sequence of wins and losses?

139. What is the value of x, if x is a whole number, in the sum below?

$$x^3 + (2x)^2 = 8 \times 3$$

Answers on page 66

OBSTACLE 21   What numbers are missing from the segments below?

140.

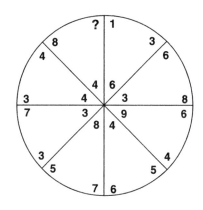

141.

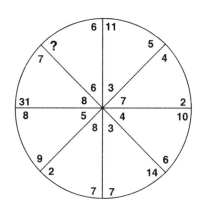

142.

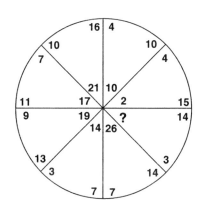

Answers on page 66

THE NUMBER JUMP

ZONE ②

OBSTACLE 22

143. If Alan gives Brenda $5.50 they will both have the same amount of money. If Brenda gives Alan $1.50, Alan will have twice as much as Brenda. What did they have at the start?

144. A child has an equal number of four different coins from 1c, 5c, 10c, 25c, 50c, and $1. If the total value is $20.28, then how many of which coins does the child have?

145. Divide 100 by one-half, and add 7. What is the answer?

146. A cube 8in x 8in x 8in is immersed in paint and then cut into half-inch cubes. How many of the cubes will have paint on:

        (a) One surface?
        (b) Two surfaces?
        (c) Three surfaces?

147. In a small town of 1000 homes, 15% have unlisted telephone numbers and 20% do not have a telephone number at all. If you select 500 numbers from the telephone directory at random, how many of those homes in that town will be unlisted?

148. Where will the symbols +, −, x and ÷ go if they are used once only to replace the question marks in the following, and what is the highest possible whole number answer?

$$4 \; ? \; 2 \; ? \; 5 \; ? \; 4 \; ? \; 9 \; =$$

149. Where will the symbols +, −, x and ÷ go if they are used once only to replace the question marks in the following, and what is the highest possible answer?

$$4 \; ? \; 5 \; ? \; 6 \; ? \; 3 \; ? \; 7 \; =$$

150. You throw three darts at this strange dartboard. How many ways are there to score 50 without a miss and no set of three numbers occurring in a different order?

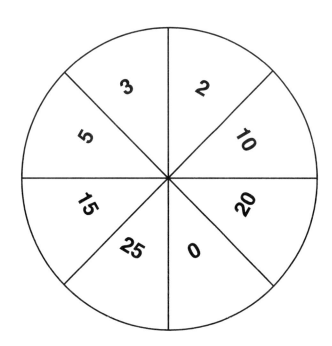

151. A car is going at 45 mph and is being followed by another car going at 40 mph. If the first car stops after 165m, how long will it take for the second car to catch up?

152. Can you determine what number should replace the question marks?

2	6	7	9	1				6	1	4	3	8				4	0	3	3	5			
8	0	2	7	6	D	F	A	9	4	4	2	3	B	I	H	?	?	?	?	?	G	C	E
5	3	0	2	4				3	2	6	8	7				1	9	7	8	1			

Answers on page 67

ZONE ②

ANSWERS

OBSTACLE 1

1. Player 2.
2. Player 3.
3. Player 6.
4. Player 3.
5. Players 1, 2 and 6.
6. Players 1, 2, 4 and 6.
7. 21.
8. 51.

OBSTACLE 2

9. 50.
10. 20.
11. 1280.
12. 1170.

OBSTACLE 3

13.

 = 3   = 5   = 2   = 7   = 4   = 1   = 6

OBSTACLE 4

14. 66. Two previous numbers added.

15. 154. $(n + 3) \times 2$.

16. 9, 20. Two series + 3, + 4, + 5, etc., and + 2 each time.

17. 51. $(2n - 3)$.

18. −49. $(2n - 15)$.

19. 70. $(2n - 1^2)$, $(2n - 2^2)$, etc.

20. 343. (n x previous n) ÷ 2.

OBSTACLE 5

21. 2. $(A \times B) - (D \times E) = C$

22. 6. $(BC) + A = DE$

23. 5. (Top row – 3rd row) + 2nd row = 4th row.

OBSTACLE 6

24. 97. Position of hands (not time) with hour hand, first, expressed as a sum.
113 – 16 = 97.
Others are: 51 + 123 = 174, 911 + 82 = 993.

25. 36. Position of hands (not time), expressed as minute hand – hour hand, then do sum.
(2 – 11) [–9] x (8 – 12) [–4] = 36.
Others are: (12 – 3)[9] x (7 – 5) [2] = 18, (6 – 2) [4] x (8 – 1) [7] = 28.

26. 16. Sum of segment values of shaded parts.

27. 216. Position of hands (not time), added together, then do sum.
(3 + 9) [12] x (12 + 6) [18] = 216.
Others are: (12 + 6) [18] + (6 + 3) [9] = 27, (12 + 9) [21] – (9 + 6)[15] = 5.

OBSTACLE 7

28.

5		3
1		6

Move clockwise by the number of letters in the written number.

29.

	21	
15		34
	22	

Move clockwise by the given number minus 1.

30.

17		6
9		3

Move clockwise by the given number plus 1.

OBSTACLE 8

31. 2. Make sums: First 2 digits – Second 2 digits, then First – Second.

32. 280. First digit x Fourth digit = First and Fourth digits, Second digit x Third digit = Second and Third digits.

33. 28. First digit x Second digit = First and Second digits, and Third digit x Fourth digit = Third and Fourth Digits.

OBSTACLE 9

34.

8	7	6	8	7	12	9	1
7	12	7	6	4	3	2	14
8	9	7	8	5	7	11	1
8	8	10	7	6	16	10	1
4	9	13	4	12	2	15	6
8	5	2	2	4	9	8	15
6	9	8	14	14	8	2	1
9	6	10	5	12	1	5	17

35.

5	7	8	15	4	7	5	6
11	6	9	8	16	12	10	10
7	12	10	12	3	11	6	8
6	7	2	5	7	7	15	10
12	15	10	8	5	12	8	7
6	7	11	13	9	6	9	6
9	8	10	6	8	8	1	2
3	6	4	10	10	10	15	15

OBSTACLE 10

36. 40.

4	5	12	13
3	6	11	14
2	7	10	15
1	8	9	16

37. 36.

16	9	8	1
15	10	7	2
14	11	6	3
13	12	5	4

38. 41. The grid values are the same as for answer 37.

OBSTACLE 11

39. 37. (Top left + Top right) − (Bottom left + Bottom right).
40. 156. (Top left x Bottom right) + (Bottom left x Top right).
41. 54. (Top left x Bottom left) − (Top right x Bottom right).
42. 12. (Bottom left x Bottom right) − (Top left + Top right).
43. 68. (Top left^2 − Bottom right) + (Bottom left^2 − Top right).
44. 9. (Top left x Top right + Bottom left) ÷ Bottom right.
45. 126. (Top left + Top right + Bottom left) − Bottom right.
46. 960. (Top left x Top right x Bottom left) ÷ Bottom right.
47. 51. (Top left x Bottom right^2) − (Top right x Bottom left).
48. 114. Top left + Top right + Bottom left − Bottom right.

OBSTACLE 12

49. 17—19—22—24—28—20 = 130

50. 17—19—22—28—25—20 = 131
17—23—22—24—25—20 = 131

51. 140. 17—24—26—28—25—20

52. 127. 17—19—22—24—25—20

53. 2 ways: 17—24—26—24—25—20
17—23—22—26—28—20

Answers

OBSTACLE 13

54. 35—34—34—34—35—34—10
55. 35—32—29—28—37—33—10
  35—30—29—35—32—33—10
56. 219. 35—34—34—35—37—34—10
57. 202. 35—30—29—28—37—33—10
58. 4 ways: 35—32—29—35—37—33—10
       35—30—34—35—32—35—10
       35—33—32—34—32—35—10
       35—33—32—32—35—34—10

OBSTACLE 14

59. 29. Black = 7; White = 3; Shaded = 9.
60. 25. Black = 4; White = 5; Shaded = 6.
61. 25. Black = 5; White = 2; Shaded = 8.
62. 45. Black = 3; White = 8; Shaded = 13.
63. 17. Black = 4; White = 7; Shaded = 2.
64. 20. Black = 5; White = 3; Shaded = 4.
65. 16. Black = 5; White = 2; Shaded = 2.
66. 21. Black = 1; White = 6; Shaded = 7.
67. 47. Black = 0.8; White = 12.8; Shaded = 7.8.
68. 36. Black = 4; White = 3; Shaded = 8.

OBSTACLE 15

69. 26.
70. 36.
71. 34.
72. D4 = 70.
73. 16.
74. 4. (A6, B6).
75. ⊤ = 8   ● = 20
76. A2, C1, D6.
77. △ = 16   ⊙ = 24   ★ = 10
78. 102. D3.
79. 89.
80. 20. F6
81. 73.
82. Two, C5 and D5.

	A	B	C	D	E	F
1	28	28	32	26	16	8
2	32	●	46	46	⊤	16
3	36	44	□	64	42	34
4	26	⊤	56	54	□	40
5	16	16	34	48	●	36
6	4	4	22	32	28	28

	A	B	C	D	E	F
1	△	46	54	54	49	24
2	33	58	★	△	△	36
3	37	62	⊙	102	73	48
4	41	69	89	89	⊙	48
5	36	⊙	64	64	52	32
6	24	32	52	△	28	20

OBSTACLE 16

(In answers 83–102, n = previous number)

83.   35. (n + 3), (n + 6), (n + 9), etc.
84.   94. (2n + 3), (2n + 6), (2n + 9), etc.
85.   1125. Multiply the previous two numbers.
86.   666. (n^2 – 10).
87.   –25. (2n – 9).
88.   104. (3n – 1), (3n – 2), (3n – 3), (3n – 4), etc.
89.   360. (n x 5), (n x 4), (n x 3), etc.
90.   9. ($3n + 0^2$), ($2n + 1^2$), ($n + 2^2$), ($0 + 3^2$).
91.   –37. (3n – 7).
92.   –61. (27 – 2n).
93.   78. (2n – 5), (2n – 10), (2n – 15), (2n – 20).
94.   1280. –1(n + 1), –2(2n + 2), –3(3n + 3), –4(4n + 4).
95.   841. (7n – 6), (6n – 5), (5n – 4), (4n – 3).
96.   58. n + 11.
97.   130. (3n – 17).
98.   33. (n + 4), (n + 6), (n + 8), (n + 10).
99.   223. (3n – 5), (3n – 4), (3n – 3), (3n – 2).
100. –9. 2n – 7.
101. 116. n^2 – 5.
102. –5⅗. (n – 2) ÷ 2, (n – 4) ÷ 2, (n – 6) ÷ 2, (n – 8) ÷ 2.

OBSTACLE 17

103. 120. Sum of left x sum of right.
104. –18. (Left numbers multiplied) – (right numbers multiplied).
105. 10. ((Outside top x outside bottom) – Inside). Left side – right side.
106. 360. All digits multiplied.
107. 82. (Bottom left x Top right) + Top left + Bottom right.
108. 100. (Bottom left x Bottom right) + Top left + Top right.

OBSTACLE 18

109. A6, C5, G6.   **110.** D2.   **111.** 12.
112. 117, occurs 3 times.   **113.** 91, G1.   **114.** E4.
115. None.   **116.** None.

Answers

THE NUMBER JUMP

OBSTACLE 19

117. 175. (Window + Window) x Door.
118. 42. (Left window x Right window) – Door.
119. 71. (Left window x Door) + Right window.
120. 60. (Right window – Door) x Left window.
121. 93. Right window^2 – Left window^2 – Door.
122. 153. Door^2 – (Left window + Right window).

OBSTACLE 20

123. 48.
124. 64.
125. 8.
126. 32
127. 16.
128. 2.5.
129. 9.
130. 10.
131. 0.3.
132. 7.
133. Upside down on a calculator 0.37 reads: LEO.
134. 1 and 7.
135. None, it was full already.
136. 301.
137. 41312432 or 23421314.
138. He will have had seven wins and one loss in any order.
139. 2.

OBSTACLE 21

140. 3. Opposite segments total 30.   **141.**   25. (a x b) – c = d.

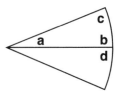

142. 18. Outside pair added = opposite one inside.

OBSTACLE 22

143. Alan $26.50, & Brenda $15.50.
144. 13 of each 1c, 5c, 50c, 100c.
145. 207.
146. a) 1176.
   b) 168.
   c) 8.
147. None, only listed numbers will be in the directory!
148. 27. Divide, plus, minus, multiply.
149. 26.6. Divide, plus, minus, multiply.
150. 5.
151. 27 minutes & 30 seconds.
152. 60851. Top row + bottom row + letter values = middle row.

SCORING SYSTEM

Do you get "Promoted" or "Busted"?

Promotion Criteria (See page 21):

Under 80	Demoted one rank.
81 - 100	No promotion.
101 - 130	Promoted one rank.
131 +	Promoted two ranks.

AGE BONUS POINTS

AGE IN YEARS	10	10.5	11	11.5	12	12.5	13	13.5	14	14.5	15	15.5
BONUS POINTS	50	45	40	35	30	25	20	16	14	12	8	4

ZONE ③

Keep a firm grip and haul yourself up to find 110 hidden meanings, letters and words.

OBSTACLE 1 In each line below match the first given word with the word that is closest in meaning, and record your answer on the answer sheet.

		A	B	C	D	E
1.	RESCUE	Retrieve	Liberate	Salvage	Redeem	Help
2.	PROTESTOR	Rebel	Dissenter	Demonstrator	Marcher	Speaker
3.	AGGRAVATE	Anger	Insult	Enrage	Provoke	Instigate
4.	ETIQUETTE	Custom	Courtesies	Example	Manners	Protocol
5.	INVOLVEMENT	Participation	Concern	Responsibility	Implication	Association
6.	HERMIT	Solitaire	Recluse	Monk	Loner	Hoarder
7.	HASSLE	Problem	Nuisance	Worry	Bother	Trouble
8.	FICTIONAL	Legendary	Invention	Informal	Genuine	Imaginary
9.	EQUIVALENT	Alike	Twin	Equal	Even	Similar
10.	FASCINATE	Catch	Charm	Captivate	Occupy	Win
11.	THRIVING	Fit	Strong	Wholesome	Flourishing	Nourishing
12.	CONFIDE	Entrust	Limit	Secret	Disclose	Speak
13.	WANDER	Saunter	Stray	Veer	Drift	Depart
14.	NOURISHING	Good	Wholesome	Healthy	Improving	Worthy
15.	ESTIMATE	Guess	Roughly	Calculate	Close	Nearly
16.	THANKLESS	Unprofitable	Useless	Ungrateful	Worthless	Unsatisfying
17.	TRADITIONAL	Fixed	Accustomed	Old	Usual	Age-long
18.	APPREHENSION	Distrust	Misgiving	Threat	Wariness	Hunch
19.	AMAZE	Bewilder	Confuse	Astonish	Startle	Stagger
20.	PROFIT	Earnings	Interest	Revenue	Gain	Value

Answers on page 72

OBSTACLE 2   Rearrange the letters given and make as many words as you can that use all of the letters. At least three words are possible from each group.

21.	A E G I L N R Y	**22.**	A E E H R T W
23.	E N O R S W	**24.**	C E I R R S T T
25.	B D E N O R S U	**26.**	A E G I L L S T
27.	A C D E I L M S	**28.**	A C H N S T
29.	A C E E R R S T	**30.**	E H I R T W
31.	E E L R S T W	**32.**	D E E R S T
33.	A D E E R R S T	**34.**	A C E L P R
35.	A D E L P	**36.**	B E E O R S V
37.	A E E N R S T	**38.**	A E L M N Y
39.	D E L M O R S	**40.**	D E G L N O

OBSTACLE 3   In each of the following groups of words a hidden common connection is present. Can you identify the connection?

41.	NARROWLY	TRAILER	GULLIBLE	JAYWALKING
42.	MARIGOLDS	JADEDNESS	EPISCOPAL	CHAMBER
43.	DISEASE	BETIDE	UNWAVERING	THREEFOLD
44.	CHROME	CORNICE	CLIMATE	BONNIEST
45.	BARNACLE	CHUTNEY	CRUSHED	CONTENTED
46.	COOKING	SHOOTER	MICROWAVE	ACRYLIC
47.	NARROWLY	GLANCED	HOAXERS	BURGUNDY
48.	ISSUE	SKIMPY	PAMPHLET	BANNER
49.	COMBATING	APPROXIMATE	OPERATE	PIGMENT
50.	CUSTARD	RISKY	HONEYMOON	MISUNDERSTAND

OBSTACLE 4   When each of the following words is rearranged, one group of letters can be used to prefix the others to form longer words. Which word is used as the prefix and what does it become?

	A	**B**	**C**	**D**
51.	RILE	COTS	MUSE	STILE
52.	SHORE	DIE	DUST	TEN
53.	FEATS	LOPE	RYE	BANE
54.	DENT	SON	LYRE	REED

Answers on pages 72 & 73

THE WORD CLIMB

55.	MAD	DEN	SAGE	LESS
56.	TOP	MOOR	EAT	LESS
57.	RED	AND	LEG	RIDE
58.	EMIT	BLEAT	STILE	RILE
59.	SHORE	HOSE	FILES	SHELF
60.	GIN	CEDES	COLA	FILED

OBSTACLE 5 Rearrange the following to form five connected words or names. What are they?

61.	TOUGHDUN	FACETIKUR	BRAGGRINDEE	CAJPALKF	CRANOOMA
62.	HETCS	RESSERD	STEETE	BALET	DAWBRORE
63.	DIALDOFF	PRONDOWS	FUNERSLOW	CHISUFA	GONEIBA
64.	OCAIR	ELOUS	HTAENS	HAGABDD	GANKKOB
65.	TREAKA	FOLG	BYGUR	DUOJ	TINDBONAM
66.	WOIBE	SORS	SCONKAJ	STRANDISE	PLESREY
67.	NARI	LICHE	RUGAPAYA	LISARE	HOLDALN
68.	PORIPNEPE	SORTITO	ZAPIZ	MAISAL	PATAS
69.	GUTTSTART	MORDDNUT	BRINLE	NOBN	GRELEBIDEH
70.	CREMRUIT	NINACNOM	NACEYEN	MUNCI	GRONEAO

OBSTACLE 6 Add the vowels in the following groups of letters to form five words, one of which does not belong with the others. Which word is the odd one out?

71.	GLV	HT	SCRF	SHWL	BRCLT
72.	DNM	KHK	NYLN	SLK	WL
73.	PLT	DSH	SCR	CHN	BKR
74.	BNGLW	FLT	HS	GRDN	MSNTT
75.	QRTT	GTR	ZTHR	TRMBN	PN
76.	DNCR	GRCR	SLR	DRVR	STDNT
77.	BLTMR	RZN	PHNX	CHCG	HSTN
78.	VDK	BRBN	GRVY	DVCT	BRNDY
79.	DMNND	LLGR	FRTSSM	HRPSCHRD	CRSCND
80.	MRYLND	NDN	NVD	GRG	BSTN

Answers on pages 73 & 74

OBSTACLE 7 Join the letters of the given words to form a single word using all of the letters.

81.	PEER	+	DAMP	**82.**	CLUE	+	PAIR
83.	MEAL	+	DIVE	**84.**	CURE	+	MAIN
85.	HALL	+	SEES	**86.**	SCENE	+	TEN
87.	RATE	+	RUSE	**88.**	ENSURE	+	DEBT
89.	WALL	+	FREE	**90.**	CANE	+	TERN

OBSTACLE 8 Each of the following words has the prefix missing. The prefix on each question is the same for all of the words in that question. Can you find the prefixes for the following?

91.	_ _ _ DOWY	_ _ _ KING	_ _ _ LLOT	_ _ _ RING
92.	_ _ _ ITAN	_ _ _ PLES	_ _ _ POSE	_ _ _ SUIT
93.	_ _ _ ADOR	_ _ _ CHED	_ _ _ INEE	_ _ _ URED
94.	_ _ _ EVER	_ _ _ DDLE	_ _ _ MACE	_ _ _ PPER
95.	_ _ _ AWAY	_ _ _ MING	_ _ _ THER	_ _ _ MERS

OBSTACLE 9 For each word shown write another word with the same meaning beginning with the letter "C".

96.	PSYCHIC		**97.**	ATROCITY
98.	ACCURATE		**99.**	OPPOSE
100.	INFORMAL		**101.**	PUNISH
102.	SLINGSHOT		**103.**	INEXPENSIVE
104.	ANGEL		**105.**	INFANT

OBSTACLE 10 In each question can you underline the two words that are nearest in meaning?

	A	**B**	**C**	**D**	**E**
106.	Encourage	Indicate	Assure	Suggest	Promise
107.	Assembly	Direction	Presentation	Construction	Preparation
108.	Early	Instant	Alert	Immediate	Efficient
109.	Prospect	Verification	Proof	Trial	Demonstration
110.	Skill	Professional	Cleverness	Readiness	Talent

Answers on pages 74 & 75

ZONE ③

ANSWERS

THE WORD CLIMB

OBSTACLE 1

1.	C.	**2.**	B.
3.	D.	**4.**	D.
5.	A.	**6.**	B.
7.	D.	**8.**	E.
9.	C	**10.**	C.
11.	D.	**12.**	A.
13.	D.	**14.**	B.
15.	C.	**16.**	C.
17.	B.	**18.**	D.
19.	C.	**20.**	D.

OBSTACLE 2

21.	Relaying, Layering, Yearling.	**22.**	Wreathe, Weather, Whereat.
23.	Owners, Worsen, Rowens.	**24.**	Stricter, Critters, Restrict.
25.	Bounders, Rebounds, Suborned.	**26.**	Legalist, Stillage, Tillages.
27.	Decimals, Medicals, Declaims.	**28.**	Stanch, Snatch, Chants.
29.	Retraces, Terraces, Caterers.	**30.**	Whiter, Wither, Writhe.
31.	Wrestle, Swelter, Welters.	**32.**	Rested, Desert, Deters.
33.	Serrated, Treaders, Retreads.	**34.**	Parcel, Carpel, Placer.
35.	Paled, Pedal, Plead.	**36.**	Observe, Obverse, Verbose.
37.	Earnest, Eastern, Nearest.	**38.**	Namely, Meanly, Laymen.
39.	Remolds, Smolder, Molders.	**40.**	Dongle, Golden, Longed.

OBSTACLE 3

41. Owl, Rail, Gull, Jay.

42. Gold, Jade, Opal, Amber.

43. Sea, Tide, Wave, Reef.

44. Rome, Nice, Lima, Bonn.

45. Barn, Hut, Shed, Tent.

46. Coo, Hoot, Crow, Cry.

47. Arrow, Lance, Axe, Gun.

48. Sue, Kim, Pam, Anne (or Ann).

49. Bat, Ox, Rat, Pig.

50. Star, Sky, Moon, Sun.

OBSTACLE 4

51. Cost, which makes Costlier, Costumes, Costliest.

52. Stud, which makes Studhorse, Studied, Student.

53. Bean, which makes Beanfeast, Beanpole, Beanery.

54. Tend, which makes Tendons, Tenderly, Tendered.

55. Dam, which makes Damned, Damages, Damsels.

56. Tea, which makes Teapot, Tearoom, Teasels.

57. Dan, which makes Dander, Dangle, Dandier.

58. Time, which makes Timetable, Timelist, Timelier.

59. Horse, which makes Horseshoe, Horseflies, Horseflesh.

60. Coal, which makes Coaling, Coalesced, Coalfield.

OBSTACLE 5

61. Doughnut, Fruitcake, Gingerbread, Flapjack, Macaroon.

62. Chest, Dresser, Settee, Table, Wardrobe.

63. Daffodil, Snowdrop, Sunflower, Fuchsia, Begonia.

64. Cairo, Seoul, Athens, Baghdad, Bangkok.

65. Karate, Golf, Rugby, Judo, Badminton.

66. Bowie, Ross, Jackson, Streisand, Presley.

67. Iran, Chile, Paraguay, Israel, Holland.

68. Pepperoni, Risotto, Pizza, Salami, Pasta.

69. Stuttgart, Dortmund, Berlin, Bonn, Heidelberg.

70. Turmeric, Cinnamon, Cayenne, Cumin, Oregano.

THE WORD CLIMB

OBSTACLE 6

71. Bracelet. Others are Glove, Hat, Scarf, Shawl.
72. Khaki. Others are Denim, Nylon, Silk, Wool.
73. China. Others are Plate, Dish, Saucer, Beaker.
74. Garden. Others are Bungalow, Flat, House, Maisonette.
75. Quartet. Others are Guitar, Zither, Trombone, Piano.
76. Student. Others are Dancer, Grocer, Sailor, Driver.
77. Arizona. Others are Baltimore, Phoenix, Chicago, Houston.
78. Gravy. Others are Vodka, Bourbon, Advocaat, Brandy.
79. Harpsichord. Others are Diminuendo, Allegro, Fortissimo, Crescendo.
80. Boston. Others are Maryland, Indiana, Nevada, Georgia.

OBSTACLE 7

81. Pampered.
82. Peculiar.
83. Medieval.
84. Manicure.
85. Seashell.
86. Sentence.
87. Treasure.
88. Debentures.
89. Farewell.
90. Entrance.

OBSTACLE 8

91. Sha.
92. Pur.
93. Mat.
94. Gri.
95. Far.

OBSTACLE 9

96. Clairvoyant.
97. Cruelty.
98. Correct.
99. Counter.
100. Casual.
101. Chastise.
102. Catapult.
103. Cheap.
104. Cherub.
105. Child.

Answers

OBSTACLE 10

106. C & E.

107. A & D.

108. B & D.

109. B & C.

110. A & E.

SCORING SYSTEM

Is Your Progress Slow?

Promotion Criteria (See page 21):

Under 50 :	"*Are you sure you should be in the Army?*" Demoted one rank.
51 - 70	"*Sorry, you must try harder.*" No promotion.
71 - 90	"*Training is going well.*" Promoted one rank.
91 +	"*Real promise shown.*" Promoted two ranks.

AGE BONUS POINTS

AGE IN YEARS	10	10.5	11	11.5	12	12.5	13	13.5	14	14.5	15	15.5
BONUS POINTS	30	25	20	18	17	16	14	12	10	8	6	3

ZONE ④

You only have a few minutes to memorize vital information. If you get forgetful now your score will plummet.

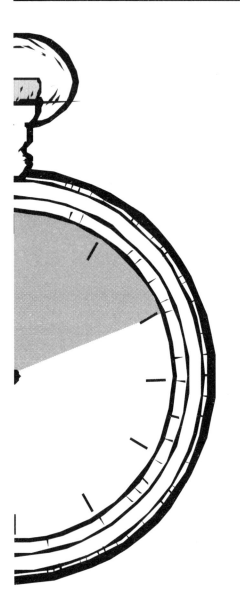

THE MEMORY TESTS

MEMORY TEST 1

Study the next page of property particulars for 2 minutes, then begin the test on the next page.

ONCE THE TEST HAS STARTED YOU
MUST NOT LOOK BACK

Set the clock and begin

Time allowed for this test
10 MINUTES

PROPERTY FOR SALE

The Old Stone House Manor,
Farmhouse Lane,
Hookey,
Worcestershire.

An eye-catching three-storey detached manor house is being sold on the outskirts of Hookey. The property dates back to Elizabethan times and over the last 10 years has been restored considerably, but retains its period atmosphere (including ceiling beams). The property is south-facing with magnificent views over the River Dean and picturesque woodland beyond. There is easy access to the A454 and the B2314.

The property is equipped with gas-fired central heating, double-glazing and a security system.

Offers around **£235,000** are being invited for this freehold home.

The three-storey property has a living room, drawing room, sitting room, breakfast kitchen, utility room, cloakroom and storeroom on the ground floor. On the first floor there are 4 bedrooms (2 with en-suites), and the main bathroom has a spa corner-bath, shower and adjoining dressing room. On the second floor you will find three more bedrooms together with a large games room. There is a large double garage joined on to the property, which is adequate to park three cars.

The property is surrounded by a courtyard, which is well established with a wide variety of shrubs and trees. The borders are well stocked and there is a vegetable patch with potatoes, carrots, lettuces, onions, garlic and broad beans. The property can be viewed by contacting the owners.

ZONE ④

1. What is the name of the house?

2. In what town is it situated?

3. Is it in Warwickshire or Worcestershire?

4. How many storeys does the property have?

5. In what part of Hookey will you find the property?

6. In what period was the house built?

7. Does the property have ceiling beams?

8. What is the asking price of the property?

9. Should you contact the agents to view the property?

10. How many bedrooms does the property have?

11. What room adjoins the main bathroom?

12. Does the bathroom have a power shower?

13. How many bedrooms are on the second floor?

14. What two main roads are within easy access to the property?

15. What river can be viewed from the property?

16. Does the property have double-glazing or secondary glazing?

17. Where will you find the games room?

18. What vegetables can be found on the vegetable patch?

19. Is there an orchard?

20. How many cars can you park in the garage?

21. Is the garage joined on to the property?

22. Does the property face south-east?

23. Apart from the river, what else can be viewed from the property?

24. Is there a drawing room on the ground floor?

25. Are there two bedrooms or three bedrooms with en-suites?

THE MEMORY TESTS

1. ....

2. ....

3. ....

4. ....

5. ....

6. ....

7. ....

8. ....

9. ....

10. ....

11. ....

12. ....

13. ....

14. ....

15. ....

16. ....

17. ....

18. ....

19. ....

20. ....

21. ....

22. ....

23. ....

24. ....

25. ....

Answers on page 104

THE MEMORY TESTS

OBSTACLE 2

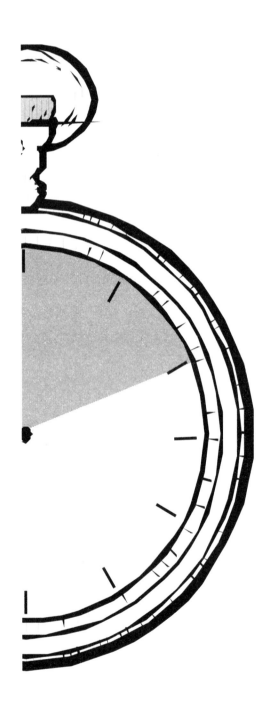

MEMORY TEST 2

Study the crossword opposite for 2 minutes, then begin the test on the next page. The crossword is made up of words for fruits, vegetables and animals.

ONCE THE TEST HAS STARTED YOU
MUST NOT LOOK BACK

Set the clock and begin

Time allowed for this test
10 MINUTES

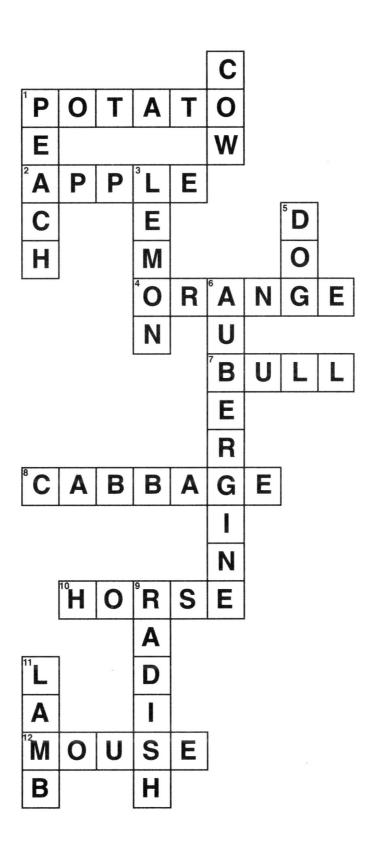

1. How many types of fruit are there?

2. How many types of animals are there?

3. How many types of vegetables are there?

4. Is 3 down a fruit or vegetable?

5. Does cabbage go across the puzzle or down it?

6. What animal is at 5 down and runs through orange?

7. Is there an onion in the crossword?

8. Are there more fruits than vegetables?

9. What animal will you find at 12 across?

10. Is there more than one dog on the crossword?

11. What item will you find at 9 down?

12. What is the longest word in the crossword?

13. How many words have five letters?

14. How many words have three letters?

15. One item in the crossword does not have a number. Which is it?

16. Can apple be found at 2 across or 3 across?

17. Where will you find bull?

18. Where will you find carrot?

19. What animal will you find at 11 down?

20. How many words are there altogether in the crossword?

THE MEMORY TESTS

1. ....

2. ....

3. ....

4. ....

5. ....

6. ....

7. ....

8. ....

9. ....

10. ....

11. ....

12. ....

13. ....

14. ....

15. ....

16. ....

17. ....

18. ....

19. ....

20. ....

Answers on page 104

ZONE ④

MEMORY TEST 3

Study the flight timetable opposite for 2 minutes, then begin the test on the next page.

ONCE THE TEST HAS STARTED YOU
MUST NOT LOOK BACK

Set the clock and begin

Time allowed for this test
10 MINUTES

Study the timetable showing departure time, destination and airline.

DEPARTURE TIME	DESTINATION	AIRLINE
0630	PARIS	BRITISH AIRWAYS
0645	SPAIN	IBERIA
0705	MOMBASSA	MONARCH
0755	FLORIDA	VIRGIN ATLANTIC
0910	CYPRUS	DELTA
0945	IRELAND	AEROFLOT
1000	CHINA	CATHAY PACIFIC
1020	JAMAICA	OLYMPIC
1245	INDIA	KLM
1300	IRELAND	IBERIA
1345	AMSTERDAM	AEROFLOT

1. How many flights are there altogether?

2. At what time is the first flight?

3. What is the destination of the flight that leaves at 09.45?

4. How many flights are there to Ireland?

5. What airline is the flight to Jamaica?

6. Which country are you flying to if you travel by Cathay Pacific?

7. What time does the flight to India leave?

8. Where would you be travelling to if you leave at 07.55 by Virgin Atlantic?

9. What time is the flight to Sydney?

10. What is the name of the airline that leaves at 12.45?

11. If you leave at 12.45, are you going to India or Ireland?

12. How many flights are there to India?

13. How many flights are there by Iberia Airlines?

14. What time is the last flight?

15. Where are you flying if you leave at 10.25?

16. Are there any flights by Aer Lingus?

17. What time is the flight to Spain?

18. If you are travelling to China, do you leave at 10.00 or 10.20?

19. Does the flight to Cyprus leave at 09.10 by Delta Airlines?

20. Does the flight to Jamaica leave at 10.10 by Olympic Airlines?

THE MEMORY TESTS

1. ....

2. ....

3. ....

4. ....

5. ....

6. ....

7. ....

8. ....

9. ....

10. ....

11. ....

12. ....

13. ....

14. ....

15. ....

16. ....

17. ....

18. ....

19. ....

20. ....

Answers on page 105

MEMORY TEST 4

Study the car park details opposite for 2 minutes, then begin the test on the next page.

ONCE THE TEST HAS STARTED YOU
MUST NOT LOOK BACK

Set the clock and begin

Time allowed for this test
10 MINUTES

ST. MARY'S CAR PARK

Opening Times: 7.30 am
to 6.30 pm

Car-parking prices:

Up to		
1 hour	**$0.50**	
2 hours	**$1.00**	
3 hours	**$1.50**	
Over 3 hours	**$2.30**	

1.

RED MINI	RED CORSA	WHITE FIESTA	SILVER AUDI	GREEN LAND - ROVER

2.

	WHITE VAN	GOLD MERCEDES	RED CORSA	GREEN PEUGEOT

3.

	BLACK ASTRA	BLACK ESCORT	BLACK BMW	YELLOW MGBT

4.

YELLOW HONDA 600			BLUE RANGE ROVER	RED PORSCHE		

ZONE ④

1. What was the name of the car park?

2. How many prices were listed on the price list?

3. How many rows of car parking spaces were there?

4. How many spaces were there altogether?

5. How many spaces were there on Row 4?

6. How many car parking spaces were unoccupied?

7. How many car parking spaces were unoccupied on Row 1?

8. How many cars were parked altogether?

9. How many red cars were there in the car park?

10. How many cream cars were there?

11. Which car was between the gold Mercedes and the green Peugeot?

12. Which car was parked in the middle of Row 1?

13. How many Corsas were there?

14. How many hours a day was the car park open?

15. What time did the car park close?

16. How many different makes of car were in the car park?

17. Was the only Escort red, white, green, blue or black?

18. Was the Range Rover green, blue or white?

19. You drive into the Car Park and go next to the Black Astra. Which row are you on?

20. What is the most popular shade of car?

21. How much does it cost you to park for 3½ hours?

THE MEMORY TESTS

1. ....

2. ....

3. ....

4. ....

5. ....

6. ....

7. ....

8. ....

9. ....

10. ....

11. ....

12. ....

13. ....

14. ....

15. ....

16. ....

17. ....

18. ....

19. ....

20. ....

21. ....

Answers on page 105

THE MEMORY TESTS

MEMORY TEST 5

Study the map opposite for 2 minutes, then begin the test on the next page.

ONCE THE TEST HAS STARTED YOU
MUST NOT LOOK BACK

Set the clock and begin

Time allowed for this test
10 MINUTES

THE MEMORY

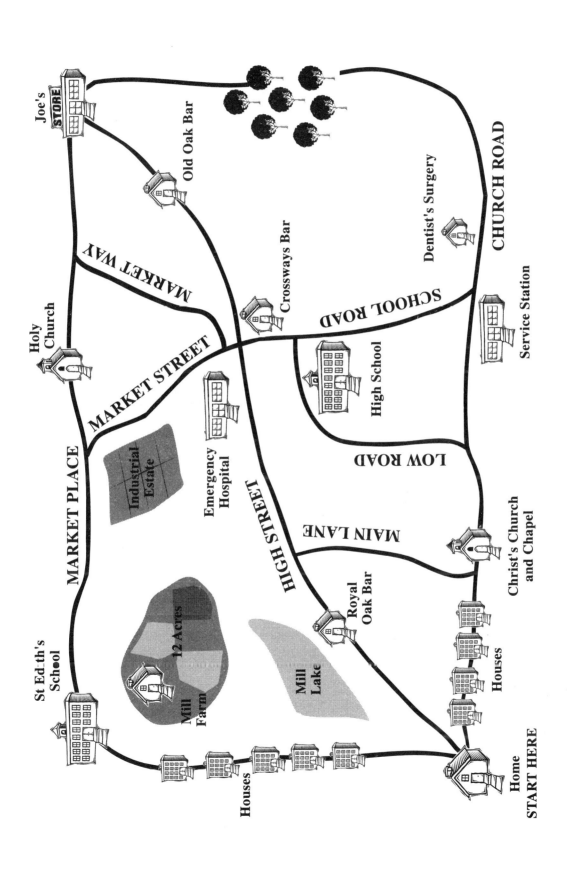

Joe's STORE

Old Oak Bar

MARKET WAY

Holy Church

MARKET STREET

MARKET PLACE

St Edith's School

Industrial Estate

Emergency Hospital

12 Acres

Mill Farm

Mill Lake

HIGH STREET

Houses

Crossways Bar

High School

SCHOOL ROAD

Dentist's Surgery

CHURCH ROAD

Service Station

LOW ROAD

MAIN LANE

Royal Oak Bar

Christ's Church and Chapel

Houses

Home
START HERE

TEST

ZONE ④

1. What is the name of the road that would take you directly to Joe's store?

2. You decide to start your journey by turning right as you leave your home. Before you reach the church you come to a left turn. What is the name of that road?

3. On what road would you find the Royal Oak bar?

4. How many bars are there on the map?

5. Is there a dentist's surgery on the map?

6. What is the name of the farm on the map?

7. How many acres of land does the farm have?

8. How many churches are there on the map?

9. Can you name the school on Market Place?

10. How many bars are there on High Street?

11. If you travel along High Street from your home, what is the name of the third bar you come to?

12. If you turn left out of your home, how many houses do you pass?

13. Is there a pond or a lake on the map?

14. Which road would you travel down if you needed to fill your car's tank?

15. If you went along High Street, would you take a left or a right to get to the dentist's surgery when you reached the second bar?

16. Name one of the two roads that meet at High School?

17. How many units are on the Industrial Estate?

18. How many roads contain the word "Market"?

19. You turn to the right from your home, pass by Christ's Church and Chapel, and take the next left. What is the name of that road?

20. Which road would you travel along if you wanted to visit Christ's Church and Chapel?

THE MEMORY TESTS

1. ....

2. ....

3. ....

4. ....

5. ....

6. ....

7. ....

8. ....

9. ....

10. ....

11. ....

12. ....

13. ....

14. ....

15. ....

16. ....

17. ....

18. ....

19. ....

20. ....

Answers on page 106

MEMORY TEST 6

Study the street plan opposite for 2 minutes, then
begin the test on the next page.

ONCE THE TEST HAS STARTED YOU
MUST NOT LOOK BACK

Set the clock and begin

Time allowed for this test
10 MINUTES

Vacant
Nº 40

POST OFFICE
Mr. J. Miller
Nº 33a

Mrs. T. Hodge
Nº 33

Miss. R. Morley
Nº 29

Mrs. N. Jackson
Nº 26

Mr. P. Field
Nº22

Mr. & Mrs. Armstrong
Nº 15

Miss D. Pearce
Nº 12

Mr. & Mrs. Dukes
Nº 10

LONGFORD HALL LANE

Derelict Property
Nº 43

Mr. L. Kennedy
Nº 35

Mr. & Mrs. Jennings
Nº 30

Mr. R. Giles & Mrs K. Sandham
Nº 28

Mr. P. Corfield
Nº 24

Vacant
Nº 19

Mr. & Mrs. Bromley
Nº 14

Mr. & Mrs. Wainwrght
Nº 11

Mr. Davies & Miss. Johnson
Nº 9

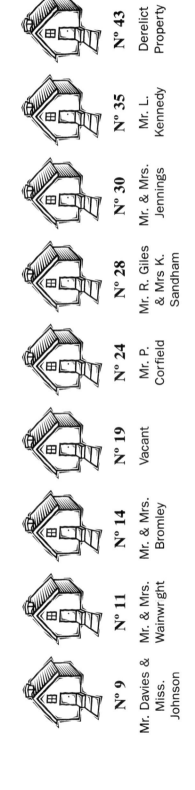

ZONE ④

1. What is the name of the street?

2. How many houses are there altogether?

3. How many houses are occupied by men only?

4. How many houses are occupied by women only?

5. What is the name of the couple who occupy No. 10?

6. Who lives at No. 22?

7. Is house No. 40 vacant?

8. Is house No. 11 vacant?

9. Who occupies the Post Office?

10. Who lives between Mr. and Mrs. Bromley and Mr. P. Corfield?

11. Is Miss Johnson one of the occupiers of No. 9?

12. What is the initial of Miss Pearce who lives at No. 12?

13. Standing on the street, who lives to the left of the Post Office?

14. Does Mr. R. Giles occupy the same house as Miss. R. Morley?

15. Who lives with Mr. L. Kennedy?

16. What number is the house opposite No. 22?

17. How many houses are unoccupied?

18. At what number does Mrs. K. Sandham live?

19. What is the number of the derelict property?

20. Does Mr. P. Field occupy No. 22?

THE MEMORY TESTS

1.

2.

3.

4.

5.

6.

7.

8.

9.

10.

11.

12.

13.

14.

15.

16.

17.

18.

19.

20.

Answers on page 106

ZONE ④

MEMORY TEST 7

Study the grid opposite for 3 minutes, then begin the test on the next page.

ONCE THE TEST HAS STARTED YOU
MUST NOT LOOK BACK

Set the clock and begin

Time allowed for this test
10 MINUTES

	1	2	3	4	5	6	
	$	¶	Q	=	¶	Ó	A
	$	¶	2	4	Ó	Ó	B
	Ó	Z	4	$	$	$	C
	3	$	=	Ó	Q	3	D
	Q	Z	¶	$	Ó	¶	E
	¶	%	=	%	&	%	F

1. What numbers go across the top of the page?

2. What letters go down the right side of the page?

3. What letter will you find in box 2C?

4. What symbol will you find in box 1A?

5. In order from the left, list the symbols that appear in row F.

6. Which symbol appears three times in row C?

7. How many boxes contain the symbol ¶?

8. Does a 4 or a $ follow Z in row C?

9. How many different numbers are there inside the table?

10. How many different letters are there inside the table?

11. In order from the top, list the symbols that appear in column 1.

12. In which row will you find three % symbols?

13. In which row will you find three $ symbols?

14. How many & symbols are in the grid?

15. What symbol can be found in box 1D?

16. Is there a Q or a $ in box 5D?

17. How many = symbols are there?

18. What letter comes before Z in row E?

19. Reading from the left, what is last symbol in row F?

20. How many of the letter Q are there?

THE MEMORY TESTS

1. ....

2. ....

3. ....

4. ....

5. ....

6. ....

7. ....

8. ....

9. ....

10. ....

11. ....

12. ....

13. ....

14. ....

15. ....

16. ....

17. ....

18. ....

19. ....

20. ....

Answers on page 107

ZONE ④

ANSWERS

Memory Test 1

1. The Old Stone House Manor.
2. Hookey.
3. Worcestershire.
4. 3.
5. The outskirts.
6. Elizabethan.
7. Yes.
8. £235,000.
9. No.
10. 7.
11. Dressing room.
12. No.
13. 3.
14. A454 and B2314.
15. River Dean.
16. Double-glazing.
17. Second floor.
18. Potatoes, Carrots, Onions, Lettuces, Garlic, Broad Beans.
19. No.
20. 3.
21. Yes.
22. No.
23. Woodland.
24. Yes.
25. 2.

Memory Test 2

1. 4.
2. 6.
3. 4.
4. Fruit.
5. Across.
6. Dog.
7. No.
8. The same.
9. Mouse.
10. No.
11. Radish.
12. Aubergine.
13. 5.
14. 2.
15. Cow.
16. 2 across.
17. 7 across.
18. You will not.
19. Lamb.
20. 14.

Memory Test 3

1. 11.
2. 06.30.
3. Ireland.
4. 2.
5. Olympic.
6. China.
7. 12.45.
8. Florida.
9. There is not one.
10. KLM.
11. India.
12. 1.
13. 2.
14. 13.45.
15. There is not a flight at 10.25.
16. No.
17. 06.45.
18. 10.00.
19. Yes.
20. No.

Memory Test 4

1. St. Mary's.
2. 4.
3. 4.
4. 22.
5. 7.
6. 6.
7. None.
8. 16.
9. 4.
10. None.
11. Red Corsa.
12. White Fiesta.
13. 2.
14. 11 hours.
15. 6.30 pm.
16. 14.
17. Black.
18. Blue.
19. Row 3.
20. Red.
21. $2.30.

THE MEMORY TESTS

Memory Test 5

1. High Street.
2. Main Lane.
3. High Street.
4. 3.
5. Yes.
6. Mill Farm.
7. 12 Acres.
8. 2.
9. St. Edith's School.
10. 3.
11. Old Oak.
12. 5.
13. A lake.
14. Church Road.
15. Right.
16. Low Road/School Road.
17. 8.
18. 3.
19. Low Road.
20. Church Road.

Memory Test 6

1. Longford Hall Lane.
2. 18.
3. 3.
4. 4.
5. Mr. and Mrs. Dukes.
6. Mr. P. Field.
7. Yes.
8. No.
9. Mr. J. Miller.
10. No one.
11. Yes.
12. D.
13. Mrs. T. Hodge.
14. No.
15. No one.
16. No. 19.
17. 3.
18. No. 28.
19. No. 43.
20. Yes.

Memory Test 7

1. 1, 2, 3, 4, 5 and 6.
2. A, B, C, D, E and F.
3. Z.
4. $.
5. ¶, %, =, %, &, %.
6. $.
7. 6.
8. 4.
9. 3.
10. 3. Ó, Z, Q.
11. $, $, Ó, 3, Q, ¶.
12. F.
13. C.
14. 1.
15. 3.
16. Q.
17. 3.
18. Q.
19. %.
20. 3.

Answers

SCORING SYSTEM

This was to see if you could get into "Special Forces"

Promotion Criteria (See page 21):

Average Paper Scores

Less than 6	*"Suggest a new trade."* Demoted one rank.
7 – 10	No progress.
11 – 14	Promoted one rank.
15 +	Promoted two ranks and selected for Special Forces.

AGE BONUS POINTS

AGE IN YEARS	10	10.5	11	11.5	12	12.5	13	13.5	14	14.5	15	15.5
BONUS POINTS	3	3	3	3	2	2	2	2	1	1	1	0

ZONE 5

The only way out of this section is to decipher 50 devious visual puzzles of logic and recognition.

OBSTACLE 1 Which of the following is the odd one out?

1.

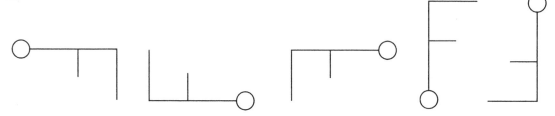

A   B   C   D   E

2.

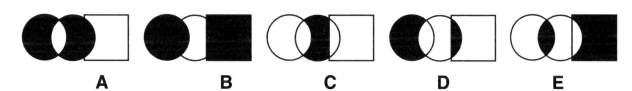

A   B   C   D   E

3.

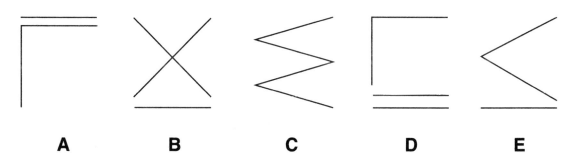

A   B   C   D   E

Answers on page 129

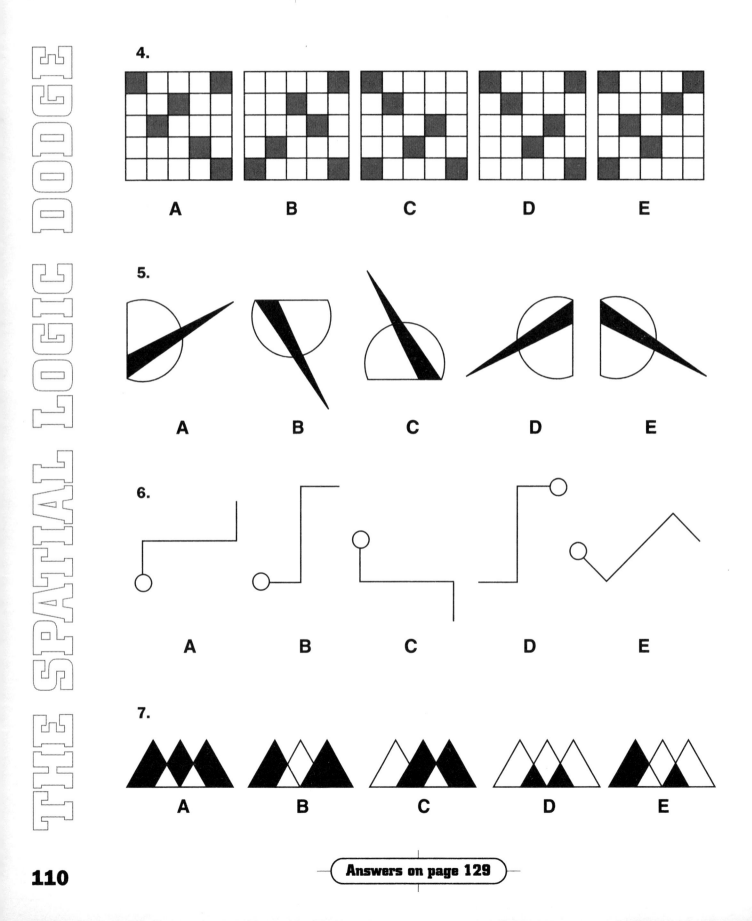

4.

A   B   C   D   E

5.

A   B   C   D   E

6.

A   B   C   D   E

7.

A   B   C   D   E

Answers on page 129

8.

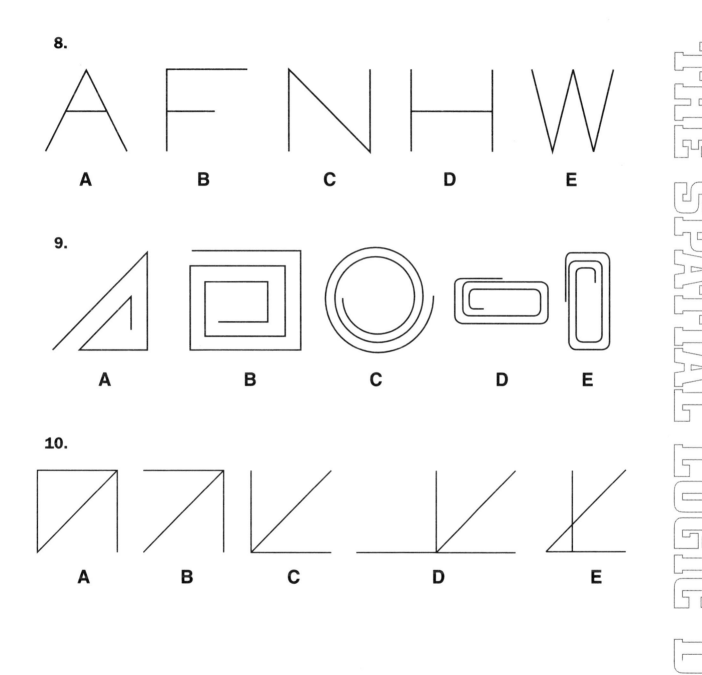

9.

10.

THE SPATIAL LOGIC DODGE

OBSTACLE 2 Which arrangement is missing from these sequences?

11.

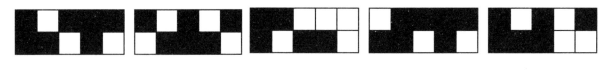

A   B   C   D   E

12.

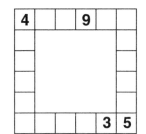   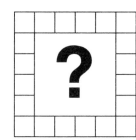   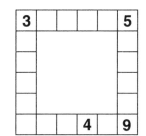

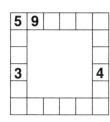   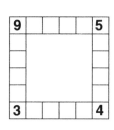   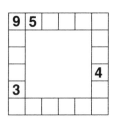   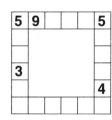

A   B   C   D   E

Answers on page 129

13.

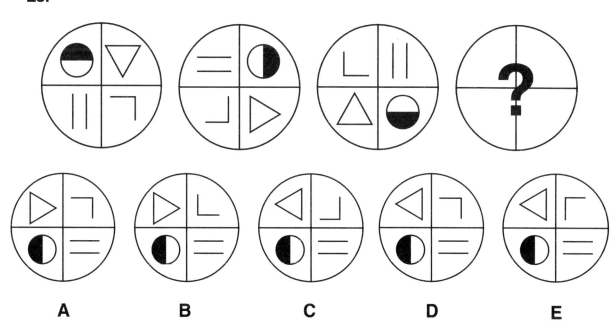

A   B   C   D   E

14.

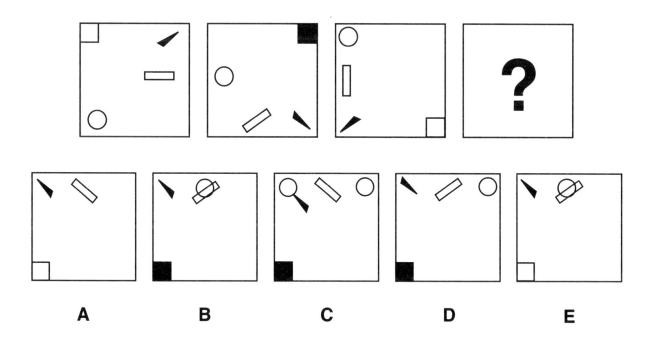

A   B   C   D   E

Answers on page 129

THE SPATIAL LOGIC DODGE

15.

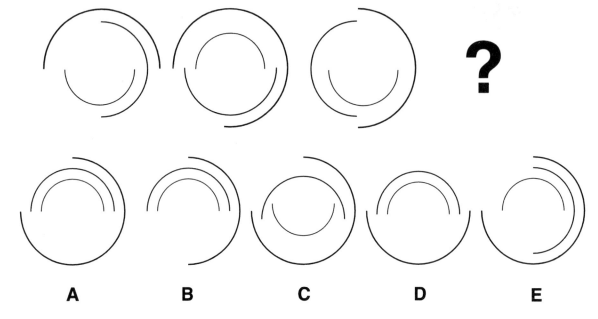

A   B   C   D   E

16.

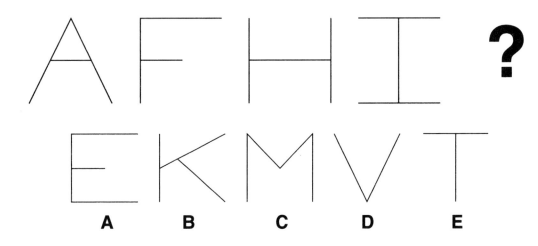

A F H I ?

A   B   C   D   E

E K M V T

17.

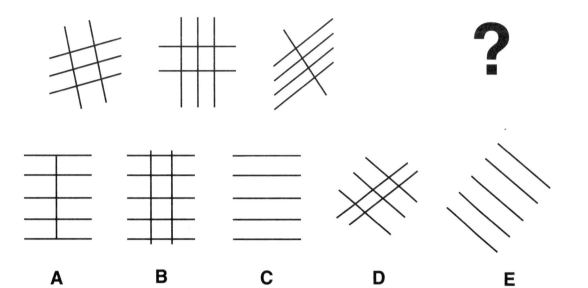

A   **B**   **C**   **D**   **E**

18.

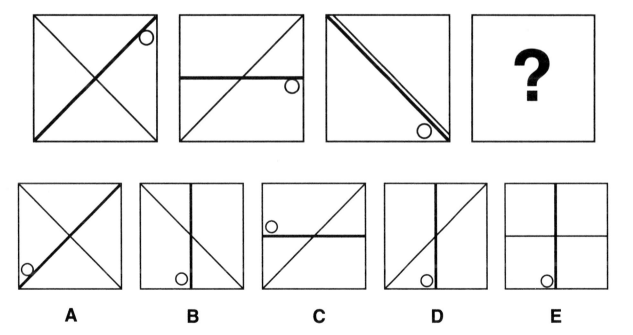

A   **B**   **C**   **D**   **E**

THE SPATIAL LOGIC DODGE

19.

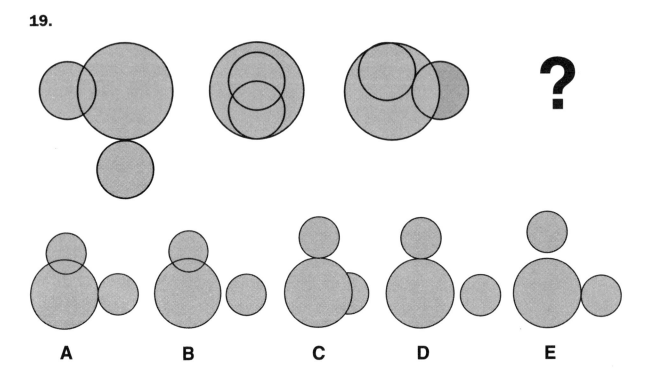

A   **B**   **C**   **D**   **E**

20.

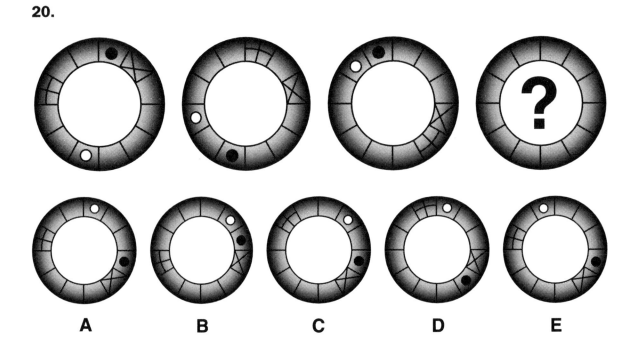

A   **B**   **C**   **D**   **E**

Answers on page 129

21.

22.

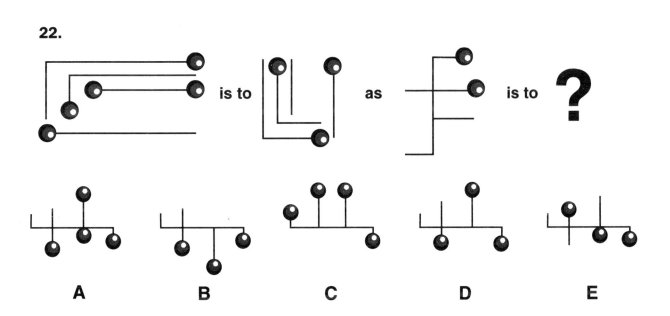

THE SPATIAL LOGIC DODGE

23.

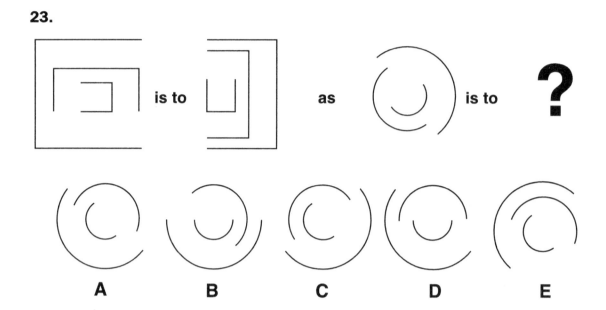

24.

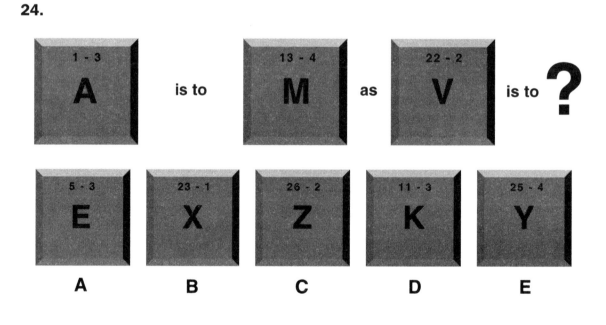

Answers on page 130

25.

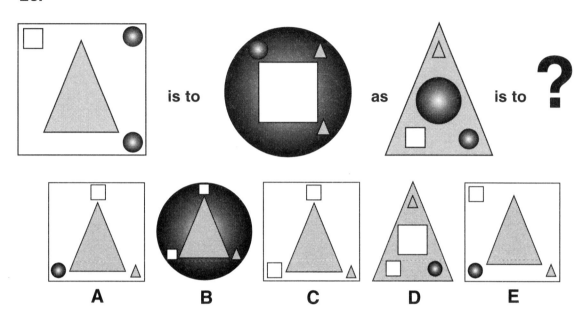

OBSTACLE 3   These are all mirror image problems. One of the 4 given images has an error on it.

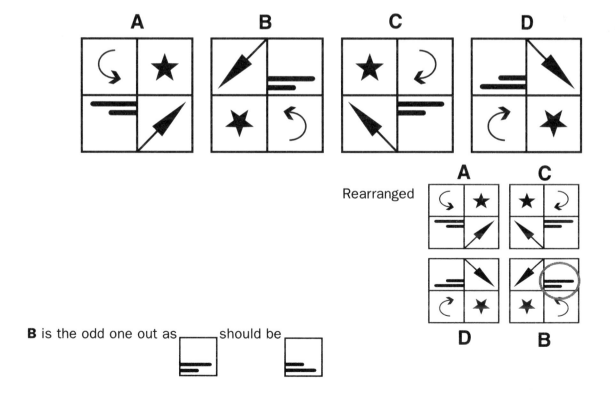

B is the odd one out as ⬜ should be ⬜

Answers on page 130

Each one of the next five puzzles is a mirror image problem. Which of A, B, C or D is the odd one out?

26.

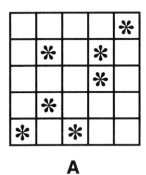

A   B

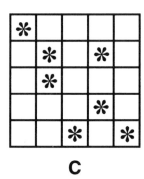

C   D

27.

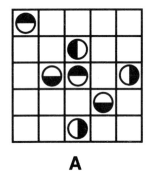

A   B

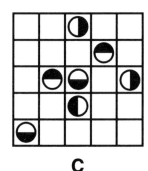

C   D

28.

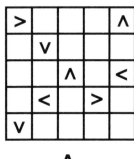

A   B

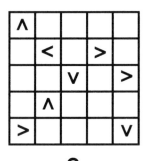

C   D

120

(**Answers on page 130**)

29.

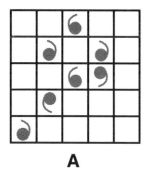

A

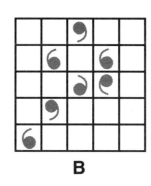

B

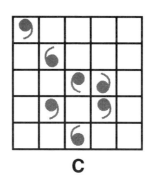

C

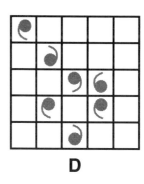

D

30.

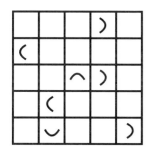

A

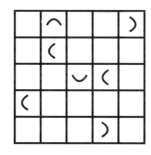

B

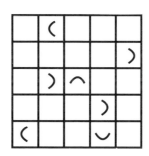

C

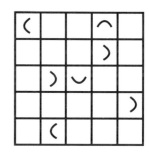

D

OBSTACLE 4   No sign is used on more than one side of the box. Which of these is not a view of the same box?

31.

A

B

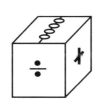

C

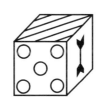

D

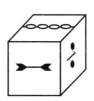

E

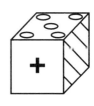

F

(**Answers on page 130**)

THE SPATIAL LOGIC DODGE

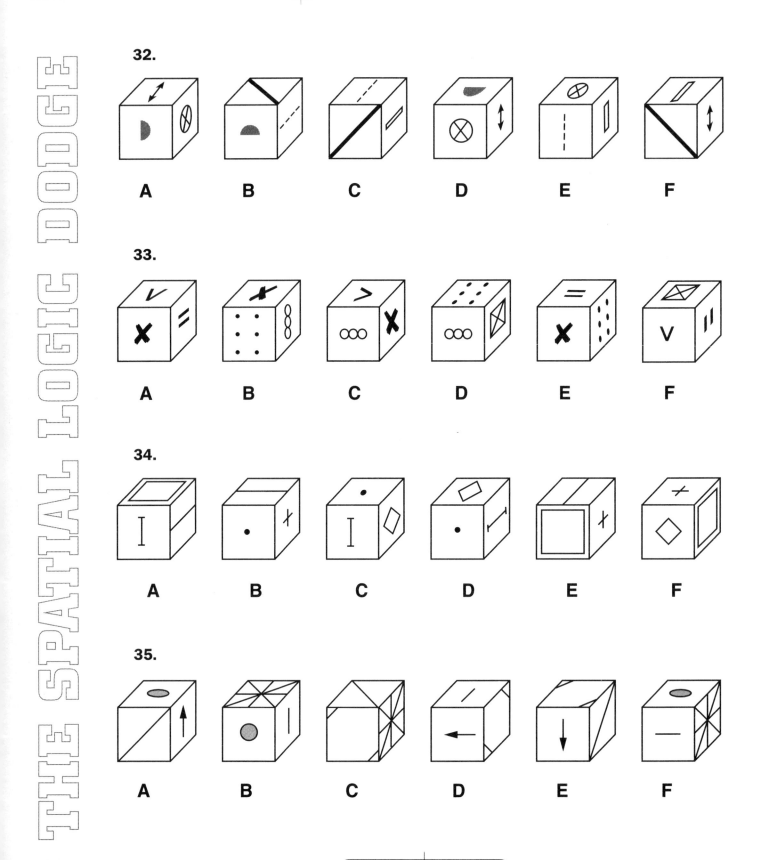

32.

A   B   C   D   E   F

33.

A   B   C   D   E   F

34.

A   B   C   D   E   F

35.

A   B   C   D   E   F

OBSTACLE 5 Which of these boxes can be made from the template? No sign is repeated on more than one side of the box.

36.

A   B   C   D   E   F

37.

A   B   C   D   E   F

Answers on page 130

THE SPATIAL LOGIC DODGE

38.

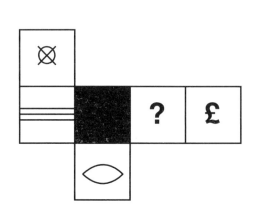

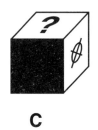

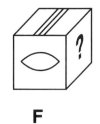

A   B   C   D   E   F

39.

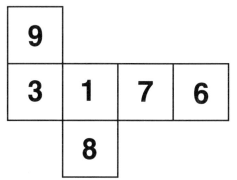

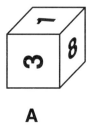

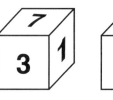

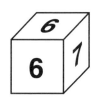

A   B   C   D   E   F

Answers on page 130

40.

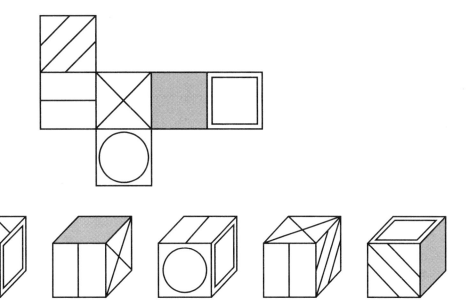

A   B   C   D   E   F

OBSTACLE 6 Can you determine which shape has not been used in these questions?

41.

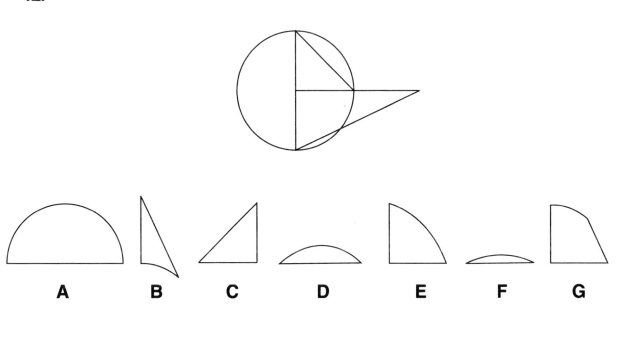

A   B   C   D   E   F   G

42.

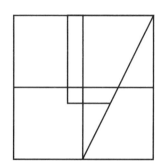

A   B   C   D   E   F   G   H   I   J

43.

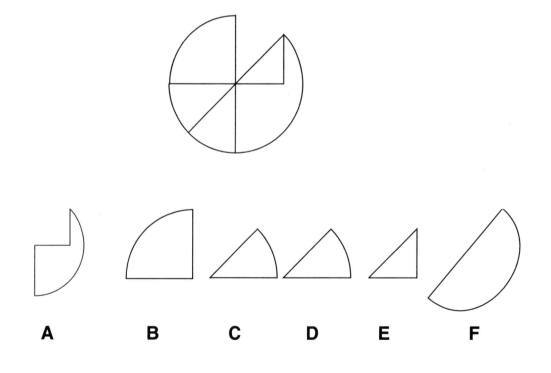

A   B   C   D   E   F

OBSTACLE 7   In the puzzles below, which shape should replace the question mark?

44.

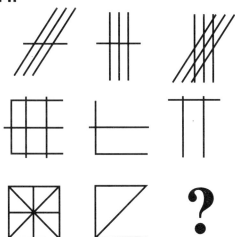

A   B   C   D   E

45.

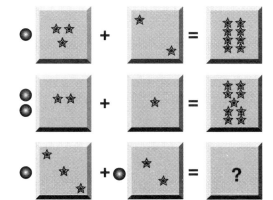

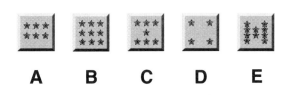

A   B   C   D   E

OBSTACLE 8   Which of the shapes – A, B, C, D or E – cannot be made from the dots if a line is drawn through all of the dots at least once?

46.

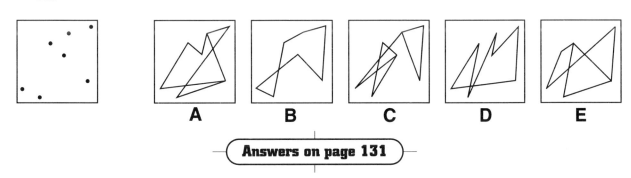

A   B   C   D   E

Answers on page 131

47.

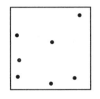 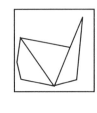 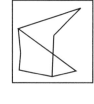   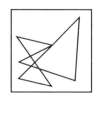

A   B   C   D   E

48.

A   B   C   D   E

49.

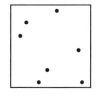 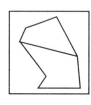   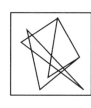 

A   B   C   D   E

50.

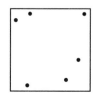     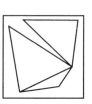

A   B   C   D   E

Answers on page 131

ZONE ⑤

ANSWERS

OBSTACLE 1

1. C. Others rotate into the same shape.
2. D. A & E and B & C form opposite pairs.
3. C. Others are Roman numerals rotated 90° anti- (counter) clockwise.
4. D. Others rotate into the same shape.
5. E. Others rotate into the same shape.
6. A. Others rotate into the same shape.
7. B. A & D and C & E form opposite pairs.
8. E. It contains four lines; the others have only three.
9. D. The pattern inside does not go clockwise.
10. E. The others are made of two shapes.

OBSTACLE 2

11. A. Binary system, start at 5 and add 3 each time. You can also find the answer by treating the images as a negative and mirror-imaging them.
12. B. Numbers rotate clockwise by the number given.
13. E. The figures rotate one sector at a time.
14. B. Shapes rotate in sequence.
15. A. Shapes rotate in sequence.
16. B. All use three lines.
17. C. Rotates and lines are subtracted from one and added to the other.
18. D. Rotating shapes.
19. D. Small circles move left to right and bottom to top.
20. A. Each shape rotates in a set sequence.

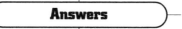

21. D. Matched opposite pairs.

22. A. Whole figure rotates 90° anti- (counter) clockwise and circles are reversed at end of lines.

23. C. Rotations in sequence.

24. D. First number is alpha-numeric position (eg, A=1).

25. A. Square becomes circle, triangle becomes square, circle becomes triangle.

OBSTACLE 3

26. D.

27. B.

28. C.

29. A.

30. A.

OBSTACLE 4

31. D.

32. B.

33. B.

34. E.

35. C.

OBSTACLE 5

36. C.

37. F.

38. E.

39. A.

40. F.

OBSTACLE 6

41. E.
42. G.
43. F.

OBSTACLE 7

44. E. Duplicated lines on first two of each row are deleted in third figure.
45. E. • = (numbers of stars x 2) + numbers of stars = number of stars in column 3.

OBSTACLE 8

46. E.
47. A.
48. D.
49. E.
50. B.

SCORING SYSTEM

The Spatial Logic Assessment

If you have done well in this section you probably have a well-organized and structured mind. Just the sort the Mind Army needs.

Promotion Criteria (See page 21):

Under 20	Busted one rank.
21 - 30	No promotion.
31 - 40	Promoted one rank.
41+	Promoted two ranks.

AGE BONUS POINTS

AGE IN YEARS	10	10.5	11	11.5	12	12.5	13	13.5	14	14.5	15	15.5
BONUS POINTS	10	10	9	8	7	6	6	5	4	3	2	1

ZONE 6

Fewer (only 151) but bigger problems this time around. You'll need a brain like a machete to cut through this undergrowth.

OBSTACLE 1 Which letter occurs once in each of the first two words but not at all in the last two words?

1.	HARMONIOUS	LIBERATE	*but not in*	MELANCHOLY	LIKE
2.	RESPECTABLE	PADDOCK	*but not in*	WATER	PRINT
3.	QUADRUPLE	PLASTIC	*but not in*	STOP	START
4.	CONVERSE	SKATEBOARD	*but not in*	INTERACT	SANDWICH
5.	DANGEROUS	HIGHLAND	*but not in*	CINDER	PARTICLE
6.	CHEMICAL	AMBASSADOR	*but not in*	DANCE	WEEKEND
7.	FIREFIGHTER	MUSHROOM	*but not in*	LENDING	REALITY
8.	GLADIATOR	DATABASE	*but not in*	FORAGE	MEDAL
9.	OCCUPATION	EXCHANGE	*but not in*	CHART	PARCEL
10.	MULBERRY	PENGUIN	*but not in*	MERCENARY	OPENING

OBSTACLE 2

11. Half of a number is three-quarters of 24. What is that number?

12. A third of a number is two-fifths of 65. What is that number?

Answers on page 146

THE DEDUCTION SCRAMBLE

133

OBSTACLE 3   Remove one letter from the first given word and place it into the second word to form two new words. You must not change the order of the letters in the words and you may not use plurals. What letter needs to move?

e.g. LEARN — FINE   (LEAN — FINER)

13.	WAIVE	—	NOSE
14.	HONEY	—	EAST
15.	OLIVE	—	CAST
16.	RIFLE	—	LAKE
17.	WAIST	—	HOOT
18.	PAINT	—	BLOT
19.	TRUST	—	DEER
20.	VITAL	—	ABLE

OBSTACLE 4   On each line, place a letter in the brackets that can be attached to the end of the word to the left and to the beginning of the word to the right to form another word in each case. No plurals are allowed.

e.g. COME (T) OWN

21.	RUIN	( )	RANT
22.	BOOT	( )	EEL
23.	TAN	( )	NOT
24.	LEAN	( )	HIGH
25.	THEM	( )	VERY
26.	SEE	( )	RAFT
27.	PAW	( )	EVER
28.	EVEN	( )	EACH
29.	LUNG	( )	LAND
30.	CAME	( )	PEN

Answers on pages 146 & 147

OBSTACLE 5 What word has a similar meaning to the first word and rhymes with the second one?

e.g. AEROPLANE — MET = JET

31.	COIN FACTORY	—	HINT	=
32.	HOME	—	BEST	=
33.	FOG	—	LIST	=
34.	BARGAIN	—	MEAL	=
35.	GRAIN	—	HORN	=
36.	PARTY	—	TALL	=
37.	BRAWL	—	HEIGHT	=
38.	RULER	—	SING	=
39.	LANTERN	—	RAMP	=
40.	BROAD	—	HIDE	=

OBSTACLE 6

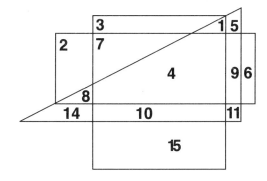

The questions below, 41–45, are about the diagram above.

41. How many numbers 1–15 appear in their own triangle?

42. Of the numbers 1–15, which numbers are missing?

43. Which number/s is/are in all three shapes?

44. From the sum of the numbers appearing in only two shapes, deduct the sum of the numbers appearing in only one shape.

45. If each numbered shape is separated from the whole, how many numbers will not be in a square, rectangle, or triangle?

Answers on page 147

OBSTACLE 7

46. Six people, A, B, C, D, E and F, are in a supermarket queue. F is not at the end of the queue, and he has two people between him and the end of the queue who is not E. A has at least 4 in front of him but is not at the end either. D is not first and has at least two behind him, and C is neither first nor last. List the order of people from the front.

OBSTACLE 8

47. From the information given, find the names and positions of the first eight to finish the marathon. Sean finishes the marathon in fourth place. He finishes after John but before Sandra. Sandra finishes before Robert but after Liam. John finishes after Rick but before Alex. Anne finishes two places after Alex. Liam is sixth to finish the race.

OBSTACLE 9 A, B, C, and D take part in school examinations. Only one sits French and that is neither B nor C. B is the only one sitting 3 tests. A sits Math and one other exam. D takes Math and English only. C sits Geography only.

48. Which exam does B not take?
49. Which person sits French?
50. Who takes Math but not English?
51. How many sit two exams?
52. Who sits English but not Geography?

OBSTACLE 10 A, B, C, D, and E take part in soccer, baseball, tennis, and swimming, of which soccer is the most popular. More choose tennis than baseball. E only plays one sport. B is the only one to take part in swimming. A and one other of the five play baseball. C does not play soccer. D plays two sports but baseball is not one of them. C plays baseball and tennis.

53. Which sport does A not take part in?
54. Who plays baseball?
55. How many play soccer?
56. Which sport do three of the five take part in?
57. How many play two of the sports only?

Answers on pages 147 & 148

OBSTACLE 11 What word, which is alphabetically between the two given words, answers the clues?

e.g. FLAP (?) FLASH Distress signal from boat (FLARE)

58.	LUMP	(?)	LUNCH	*Relating to moon*
59.	MILK	(?)	MIME	*Birdseed*
60.	ESTRANGE	(?)	ETHIC	*Endless*
61.	DEPENDENT	(?)	DEPLORE	*Exhaust*
62.	HERALD	(?)	HERD	*Plant-eating animal*
63.	CONTEMPT	(?)	CONTEST	*Satisfied*
64.	BAGEL	(?)	BAHAMAS	*Wind instrument*
65.	NUISANCE	(?)	NUMB	*To render void*
66.	SECTOR	(?)	SEDATE	*Free from danger*
67.	MAGIC	(?)	MAGNOLIA	*Industrialist*

OBSTACLE 12 Match the word groups below with the given word. Which group completes each line? Answer A, B, C, D or E.

68. REGAL

69. CROWD

70. PYRENEES

71. MISSISSIPPI

72. ORANGE

A	B	C	D	E
Nile	Elegant	Flock	Rockies	Lime
Amazon	Stately	Litter	Alps	Grapefruit
Rhine	Majestic	Gaggle	Pennines	Lemon

Answers on page 148

ZONE 6

OBSTACLE 13

73. YOGHURT
74. TREACHEROUS
75. LIZARD
76. BERNE
77. SCALES

A	B	C	D	E
Anaconda	Butter	Toaster	Dangerous	Cairo
Alligator	Milk	Colander	Threatening	Paris
Terrapin	Cheese	Skillet	Hazardous	Athens

OBSTACLE 14

78. TEAM
79. OREGANO
80. BUTTERFLY
81. MUSSEL
82. DALMATIAN

A	B	C	D	E
Lobster	Poodle	Cayenne	Earwig	Pack
Prawn	Whippet	Caraway	Ant	Crew
Crab	Doberman	Garlic	Wasp	Herd

Answers on page 148

OBSTACLE 15

83. TRIANGLE
84. PHYSICS
85. FILE
86. AEROPLANE
87. COPPER

A	B	C	D	E
History	Saw	Train	Beige	Tripod
Biology	Hammer	Bus	Maroon	Trio
Geometry	Chisel	Car	Violet	Triplet

OBSTACLE 16

88. TRAWLER
89. ARTICHOKE
90. CHICKEN
91. TINY
92. HAIL

A	B	C	D	E
Turnip	Snow	Canoe	Minute	Falcon
Pepper	Ice	Dingy	Small	Puffin
Cabbage	Frost	Barge	Short	Pigeon

Answers on pages 148 & 149

OBSTACLE 17 The map below gives the location of 6 towns A, B, C, D, E and F, but they are not in any given order. D is south-west of B and south of E. C is northeast of A and east of F. E is southeast of F and west of B.

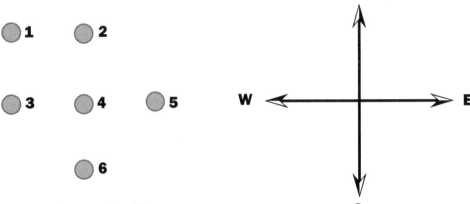

93. Which town is at point 2?
94. Which town is furthest south?
95. Which town is northwest of E?
96. Which town is at point 3?
97. Which town is furthest east?
98. Which town is due south of B

OBSTACLE 18 A certain month has five Thursdays in it and the date of the second Sunday is the 13th.

99. What is the date of the third Tuesday?
100. What is the date of the last Friday in the month?
101. What is the date of the first Monday in the month?
102. How many Saturdays are in the month?
103. What is the date of the second Friday in the month?

Answers on page 149

OBSTACLE 19 Three neighbors, Harry, Fred, and Paul, each have three cars, one two-door, one four-door, and one five-door. They each own a Buick, a Ford, and a Toyota. None of the same make of cars has the same number of doors. Harry's Buick has the same number of doors as Fred's Ford. Paul's Buick has the same number of doors as Harry's Ford. Harry's Toyota is a two-door and Fred's Toyota is a four-door.

104. Who has a five-door Toyota?
105. Who has a five-door Ford?
106. Who has a two-door Ford?
107. Who has a four-door Buick?
108. Who has a five-door Buick?
109. Who has a two-door Buick?

OBSTACLE 20 Maria, Peter and Sarah each have a dog, a cat, and a rabbit, one fluffy-tailed, one short-tailed and one long-tailed. None of the same type of animal has a tail the same as another animal, Sarah's cat has the same type of tail as Peter's rabbit. Maria's rabbit has the same tail type as Peter's cat. Sarah's dog has a long tail, and Maria's cat is fluffy-tailed.

110. Who has a dog with a short tail?
111. Who has a rabbit with a long tail?
112. Who has a dog with a fluffy tail?
113. Who has a cat with a short tail?
114. Who has a cat with a long tail?
115. Who has a rabbit with a short tail?

OBSTACLE 21 The numbers on the right are formed from the numbers on the left using the same rules. Discover the rule used and replace the question marks.

116.

3	⟶	15
5	⟶	23
8	⟶	35
9	⟶	?

117.

3 ⟶ 2
9 ⟶ 6
18 ⟶ 12
24 ⟶ ?

118.

3 ⟶ 8
9 ⟶ 10
15 ⟶ 12
24 ⟶ ?

119.

2 ⟶ 7
5 ⟶ 28
7 ⟶ 52
11 ⟶ ?

120.

2 ⟶ 4
4 ⟶ 32
5 ⟶ $62\frac{1}{2}$
7 ⟶ ?

121.

2 ⟶ 10
3 ⟶ 13
7 ⟶ 25
11 ⟶ ?

122.

4 ⟶ 18
6 ⟶ 32
9 ⟶ 53
13 ⟶ ?

123.

1 ⟶ $1\frac{1}{2}$
4 ⟶ 6
8 ⟶ 12
20 ⟶ ?

124.

2 ⟶ 2
6 ⟶ 4
8 ⟶ 5
14 ⟶ ?

Answers on page 150

125.

3	⟶	2
7	⟶	10
9	⟶	14
22	⟶	?

126.

$\frac{1}{2}$	⟶	14
1	⟶	16
3	⟶	24
5	⟶	?

OBSTACLE 22

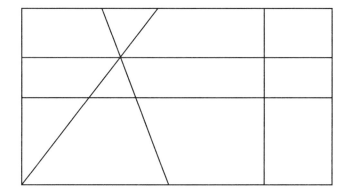

Answer the following questions on the above figure.

127. How many triangles are contained in the drawing?

128. How many right angles can be seen in the drawing?

129. How many sets of parallel lines are there going from side to side or top to bottom?

130. How many different sections are there?

131. How many squares or rectangles are there?

THE DEDUCTION SCRAMBLE

THE DEDUCTION SCRAMBLE

OBSTACLE 23 The table below shows the numbers of medals won by different regions at a sports meeting. Assume every event had a gold, silver, and bronze medal-winner with no tied results.

	GOLD	SILVER	BRONZE
REGION A	33	21	63
REGION B	72	8	20
REGION C	27	60	36

132. Which region won half the number of bronze medals as Region B won in gold medals?
133. Which region won three times as many bronze medals as Region A won in silver medals?
134. Which region won one-fifth of its total in bronze medals?
135. The sum of which two regions' gold medals matched the silver medals won by Region C?
136. If there were two other regions competing and they won only 12 gold medals between them, how many silver medals and bronze medals did they get between them?

OBSTACLE 24 Find a word that begins with the letter R that is opposite in meaning to the given word.

137. FORGETFUL
138. ORDERED
139. OCCASIONAL
140. UNPREPARED
141. CAPTURE

Answers on page 150

OBSTACLE 25

142. PARIS *is to* FRANCE *as* LONDON *is to*:

    JAPAN   AMERICA   GREECE   ENGLAND

143. NILE *is to* EGYPT *as* MAIN *is to*:

    AUSTRIA   FRANCE   ENGLAND   GERMANY

144. TEN *is to* PENTAGON *as* EIGHT *is to*:

    HEXAGON   OCTAGON   SQUARE   TRIANGLE

145. FLOOD *is to* RAIN *as* DULL *is to*:

    SUN   CLOUD   SNOW   ICE

146. HAND *is to* WRIST *as* FOOT is *to*:

    KNEE   ARM   CALF   ANKLE

147. GREEN *is to* EMERALD *as* BLUE *is to*:

    DIAMOND   SAPPHIRE   RUBY   GARNET

148. RABBIT *is to* BUCK *as* TURKEY *is to*:

    STAG   COCK   ROOSTER   GANDER

149. IRIS *is to* EYE *as* CILIA *is to*:

    HAIR   SKIN   BONES   TEETH

150. IO *is to* JUPITER *as* GANYMEDE *is to*:

    MERCURY   SATURN   VENUS   URANUS

151. CALORIE *is to* ENERGY *as* LUMEN is to:

    ELECTRICITY   PRESSURE   LIGHT   HUMIDITY

THE DEDUCTION SCRAMBLE

Answers on page 150

ZONE ⑥

ANSWERS

OBSTACLE 1

1.	R.	**2.**	C.
3.	L.	**4.**	O.
5.	G.	**6.**	M.
7.	H.	**8.**	T.
9.	N.	**10.**	U.

OBSTACLE 2

11. 36.
12. 78.

OBSTACLE 3

13. I. (Wave – Noise).
14. Y. (Hone – Yeast).
15. O. (Live – Coast).
16. F. (Rile – Flake).
17. S. (Wait – Shoot).
18. A. (Pint – Bloat).
19. T. (Rust – Deter).
20. T. (Vial – Table).

OBSTACLE 4

21. G. Makes Ruing and Grant.
22. H. Makes Booth and Heel.
23. K. Makes Tank and Knot.
24. T. Makes Leant and Thigh.
25. E. Makes Theme and Every.
26. D. Makes Seed and Draft.
27. N. Makes Pawn and Never.
28. T. Makes Event and Teach.
29. E. Makes Lunge and Eland.
30. O. Makes Cameo and Open.

OBSTACLE 5

31. Mint.
32. Nest.
33. Mist.
34. Deal.
35. Corn.
36. Ball.
37. Fight.
38. King.
39. Lamp.
40. Wide

OBSTACLE 6

41. 3.
42. 12 and 13.
43. 4.
44. −21.
45. 4.

OBSTACLE 7
46. 1st, E; 2nd, C; 3rd, F; 4th, D; 5th, A; 6th, B.

OBSTACLE 8

47. 1st, Rick; 2nd, John; 3rd, Alex; 4th, Sean; 5th, Anne; 6th, Liam; 7th, Sandra; 8th, Robert.

OBSTACLE 9

48. French.
49. A.
50. A.
51. Two.
52. D.

OBSTACLE 10

53. Swimming.
55. Four.
57. Three.

54. A and C.
56. Tennis.

OBSTACLE 11

58. Lunar.
60. Eternal.
62. Herbivore.
64. Bagpipes.
66. Secure.

59. Millet.
61. Deplete.
63. Content.
65. Nullify.
67. Magnate.

OBSTACLE 12

68. B.
70. D.
72. E.

69. C.
71. A.

OBSTACLE 13

73. B.
75. A.
77. C.

74. D.
76. E.

OBSTACLE 14

78. E.
80. D.
82. B.

79. C.
81. A.

OBSTACLE 15

83. E.
85. B.
87. D.

84. A.
86. C.

Answers

OBSTACLE 16

88. C.   **89.** A.
90. E.   **91.** D.
92. B.

OBSTACLE 17

93. C.   **94.** D.
95. F.   **96.** A.
97. B.   **98.** None.

OBSTACLE 18

99. 15th.   **100.** 25th.
101. 7th.   **102.** Four.
103. 11th.

OBSTACLE 19

104. Paul.   **105.** Fred.
106. Paul.   **107.** Paul.
108. Harry.
109. Fred.

OBSTACLE 20

110. Maria.   **111.** Maria.
112. Peter.   **113.** Sarah.
114. Peter.   **115.** Peter.

ZONE ❻

THE DEDUCTION SCRAMBLE

OBSTACLE 21

116.	39. (x 4) + 3.	**117.**	16. (x 2) ÷ 3.
118.	15. (÷ 3) + 7.	**119.**	124. n^2 + 3.
120.	171½. n^3 ÷ 2.	**121.**	37. (x 3) + 4.
122.	81. (x 7) – 10.	**123.**	30. (x 6) ÷ 4.
124.	8. (÷ 2) + 1.	**125.**	40. (– 2) x 2.
126.	32. (+ 3) x 4.		

OBSTACLE 22

127.	6.	**128.**	24.
129.	9.	**130.**	12.
131.	18.		

OBSTACLE 23

132.	C.	**133.**	A.
134.	B.	**135.**	A and C.
136.	55 silver, 25 bronze.		

OBSTACLE 24

137.	Retentive.	**138.**	Random.
139.	Regular.	**140.**	Ready.
141.	Release.		

OBSTACLE 25

142.	England.	**143.**	Germany.
144.	Square.	**145.**	Cloud.
146.	Ankle.	**147.**	Sapphire.
148.	Cock.	**149.**	Hair.
150.	Saturn.	**151.**	Light.

150

SCORING SYSTEM

Are you officer material?

Promotion Criteria (See page 21):

Under 90	Demoted again!
91 – 110	Sorry, it's tough at the top. No promotion.
111 – 130	Promoted one rank.
131 +	Promoted two ranks.

AGE BONUS CHART

AGE IN YEARS	10	10.5	11	11.5	12	12.5	13	13.5	14	14.5	15	15.5
BONUS PIONTS	30	25	22	20	18	16	14	12	10	8	6	4

ZONE ⑦

Just as many hurdles (150), but someone's raised the height!

OBSTACLE 1 Six children invent a game with dice, where the winner is the person with the highest score. The only rules are that if the same score is obtained by any other person in the round, both their round scores are doubled. Anyone rolling a double has their round score deducted.

Rolling a double and having the same rolled total as another player will give you a minus total that is double the rolled value. A thrown double is denoted by an *.

Player	round 1	round 2	round 3	round 4	round 5
A	7	7	4*	9	10
B	5	8	9	6*	9
C	9	11	5	8*	6
D	8	8*	6	4	11
E	10	9	7	5	6
F	6	4	5	11	8

When the scores are adjusted for the children's rules, which player:

1. Came third?
2. Won?
3. Came last?
4. Was winning after round three?
5. Had an even score?
6. Had a score divisible by 5 (with no remainder)?

Answers on page 178

OBSTACLE 2   A farmer has a total of 224 animals. He has 38 more sheep than cows and 6 more cows than pigs.

7. How many pigs has he?

8. How many sheep has he?

9. If he swaps 75% of his cows for 5 sheep per cow, how many sheep will he have?

10. How many animals will he have when he has made the swap in question 9 above?

OBSTACLE 3   The graph below shows the examination results of students taking their school leaving exams. 30 children took tests.

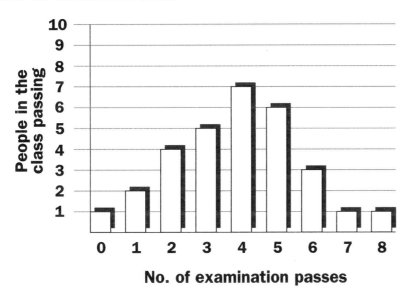

11. What was the average number of exam passes per student?

12. If the top 5 students were not in this class, what would have been the average number of exam passes per student?

13. If 10% took 8 tests, 70% took 6 tests and 20% took 4 tests, how many test papers had a fail mark?

(Answers on page 178)

ZONE ⑦

OBSTACLE 4 What number should replace the question mark and what are the values of the symbols?

14.

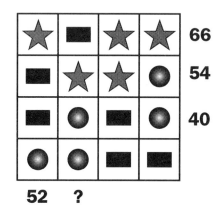

OBSTACLE 5 What numbers should replace the question marks in these sequences?

15.	1	5	10	50	100	?	?	
16.	3	8	23	68	?			
17.	3	18	63	198	?			
18.	8	5	4	9	1	7	?	?	?
19.	4	10	22	46	94	?		
20.	6	9	14	21	30	?		

OBSTACLE 6 What number should replace the question mark?

21.

154

(**Answers on pages 178 & 179**)

22.

7935	2765	1755
6188	5368	3604
9856	5488	?

23.

6459	5204	200
7288	5166	360
9768	7422	?

OBSTACLE 7 What numbers should replace the question marks in these boxes?

24.

A	B	C	D	E
3	1	4	7	9
7	0	2	8	6
6	5	1	4	7
2	2	3	9	?

Answers on page 179

25.

A	B	C	D	E
8	2	6	3	4
5	3	4	2	3
9	1	7	3	5
7	6	8	3	?

26.

A	B	C	D	E
1	5	6	2	7
4	1	5	8	9
7	3	2	6	9
6	2	?	4	?

OBSTACLE 8 How many circles are missing from the boxes with the question marks?

27.

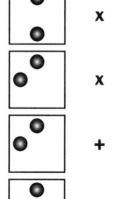

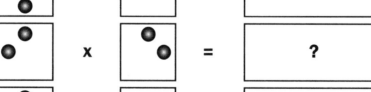

Answers on page 179

28.

z	+	w	=	00
z	x	w w z	=	00000
z z	–	w	=	000
z z z	x	w w w	=	?

29.

★	÷	n	=	0
2(★	x	2n)	=	0000 0 0000
2(★ ★	–	2n)	=	000
★	+	6n	=	?

Answers on page 179

ZONE ⑦

OBSTACLE 9 What numbers should replace the question marks?

30.

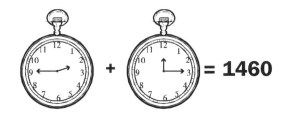

31.

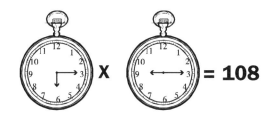

32.

Answers on page 180

33.

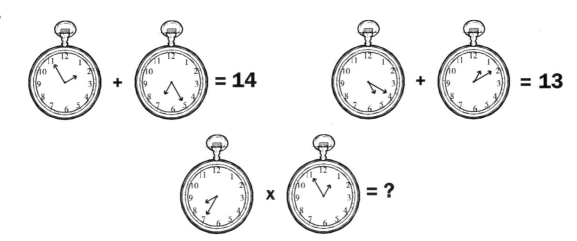

OBSTACLE 10 Divide these two grids into SIX identical shapes. The sum of the numbers in each section must give the total shown.

34.

Total 100

18	6	4	30	47	29
45	30	6	18	17	2
1	21	1	42	23	5
3	28	7	17	1	6
44	4	32	43	30	40

35.

Total 18

6	2	3	4	4	3
3	5	5	2	6	2
5	3	1	3	5	0
2	4	5	3	0	5
3	3	4	6	6	5

Answers on page 180

THE NUMBER STRADDLE

OBSTACLE 11 Divide these two grids into FOUR identical shapes. The sum of the numbers in each section must give the total shown.

36. Total 45

3	6	3	4	4	6
4	4	7	2	8	3
5	8	5	5	6	7
6	5	3	7	8	2
8	3	1	6	5	4
2	7	8	7	5	3

37. Total 55

3	6	4	4	8	6
9	6	6	7	9	2
5	6	5	6	2	7
7	6	7	5	9	3
8	9	4	8	9	7
4	9	6	8	4	6

OBSTACLE 12 What number should replace the question marks in these grids?

38.

6	4	6	5	8
2	9	8	2	1
5	0	3	4	7
3	2	1	3	1
4	7	?	4	3

39.

3	8	7	4	5
5	9	2	6	1
3	2	5	3	7
6	9	3	7	2
1	4	?	1	8

40.

1	5	3	1	2
7	6	7	6	9
2	2	3	1	9
9	9	5	9	4
4	3	?	3	7

41.

7	9	7	8	6
3	5	6	4	1
3	2	3	3	5
7	7	2	7	9
5	6	?	5	8

OBSTACLE 13   The numbers in the left-hand box move clockwise around the square to the positions shown in the box on the right. In which positions should the missing numbers appear?

42.

11	16	34
23		55
14	63	21

16		11
63		23

43.

5	2	6
7		9
12	4	3

	6	
7		12
	9	

44.

26	32	15
48		83
52	19	41

83		32
15		26

OBSTACLE 14   The values of grids A and B are given. What is the value of each of the C grids?

45.   A   B   C

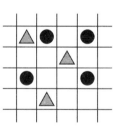   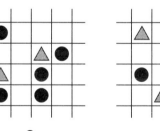

10   9   ?

46.   A   B   C

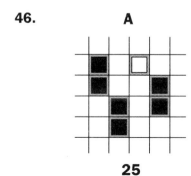   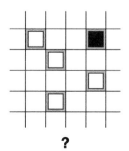

25   20   ?

(Answers on pages 182 & 183)

THE NUMBER STRADDLE

47.

A	B	C

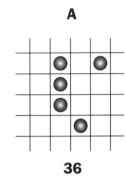

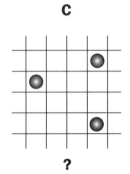

36   48   ?

OBSTACLE 15 In the number grids below each of the symbols represents a different value. The value of this symbol is also given to all its adjacent squares, including its diagonals. Half that value is also added to the squares adjacent to them (see examples below). Where two or more symbols have overlapping values the sum of those numbers are used. Values of symbol squares are not affected by such numbers from other symbols.

	A	B	C	D	E	F
1	2	2	2	2	0	0
2	4	4	4	2	0	0
3	4	✕	4	2	0	0
4	4	4	4	2	0	0
5	2	2	2	2	0	0
6	0	0	0	0	0	0

+

	A	B	C	D	E	F
1	0	5	5	5	5	5
2	0	5	10	10	10	5
3	0	5	10	△	10	5
4	0	5	10	10	10	5
5	0	5	5	5	5	5
6	0	0	0	0	0	0

=

	A	B	C	D	E	F
1	2	7	7	7	5	5
2	4	9	14	12	10	5
3	4	✕	14	△	10	5
4	4	9	14	12	10	5
5	2	7	7	7	5	5
6	0	0	0	0	0	0

If ✕ = 4   and   △ = 10, the grid value would look like the example.

C1 = (D3 x ½) + (B3 x ½) = 7
A5 = B3 x ½ = 5
D4 = D3 + (B3 x ½) = 12

(**Answer on page 182**)

48. You are faced with the matrix shown below. Can you calculate the values of each of the symbols and then answer the following questions?

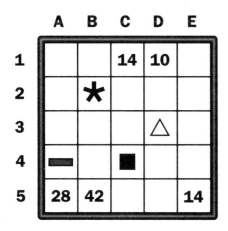

49. What is the value of square B4?
50. What is the value of square C3?
51. What is the value of square A3?
52. How many squares have the value 20?

53. Now try this more difficult grid. Can you calculate the values of the symbols?

	A	B	C	D	E	F
1			31			
2		■				17
3		*		△		
4	53				■	
5		*	△			
6	30					

54. What is the value of square C2?
55. What is the value of square D4?
56. What is the value of square B6?
57. What is the value of the highest square?
58. What is the sum of the boxes in row 1 and column A combined? Count box A1 only once.

THE NUMBER STRADDLE

OBSTACLE 16

59. If David gives Mary $4, he will have twice as much as Mary. If Mary gives David $2, David will have 11 times as much as Mary. What did they have at the start?

60. Using each of the symbols +, −, x and ÷ once only, how can you make the following sum work?   2 ? 6 ? 7 ? 4 ? 9 = 24

61. $\sqrt{64}$ is to $\frac{1}{8}$ as 4 is to ?

62. If C J is 310 and L P is 1216, what does G R equal?

63. If D J = 40 and F K = 66, what does H Q equal?

64. A car has a hole in the base of its fuel tank that leaks petrol at a rate of 1.5 gallons per hour. The car starts with a full tank of fuel (10 gallons) and averages 60 miles per hour until it runs out of fuel. The average fuel consumption, without losses caused by the leak, is 30 miles per gallon. How far will the car travel before it runs out of fuel?

65. If the hole in the tank on the car above was halfway up the tank, how far would the car have gone?

66. If it is 26 miles to London and 23 miles to Rome, how many miles is it to Moscow?

67. What three consecutive numbers when squared add up to 365?

68. What three cubed numbers when added = 9^3 (nine cubed)?

69. What number is next in this sequence?
       10   6   13   1   13   ?

70. What are the values of A, B and C in this sum if B is less than twice C and zero cannot be used?

```
A  B  C
A  A  B  +
─────────
B  A  A
```

THE NUMBER STRADDLE

71. Three-quarters of a number is two-thirds of 63. What is that number?

72. Two-fifths of three-quarters of a number is 19.2. What is that number?

73. The square root of a number is twice the cube root of 125. What is that number?

74. The square root of a number minus 10 is the fourth root of 16. What is that number?

75. Six times a number is half the square root of 144. What is that number?

76. Three-fifths of two-thirds of a number is twice the square root of 81. What is that number?

77. Half of a number is three times the cube root of 125. What is that number?

78. Five times a number is two-thirds of 66. What is that number?

79. Half of one-quarter of a number is eight times the square root of 8. What is that number?

80. Two-thirds of three-quarters of a number is 17. What is that number?

OBSTACLE 17 Start at the top left circle and move clockwise to find the value of the circle with the question mark in it.

81.

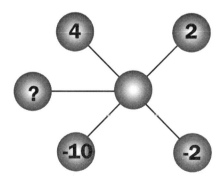

82.

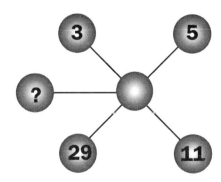

83.

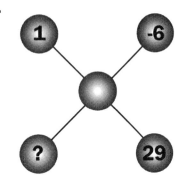

84.

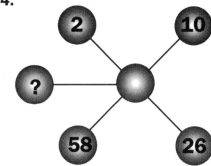

85.

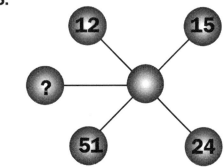

86.

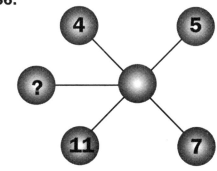

87.

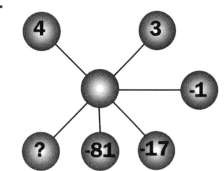

88.

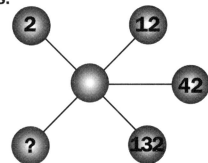

89.

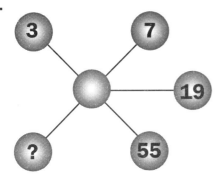

90.

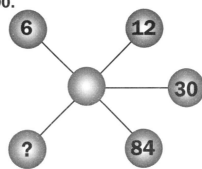

91.

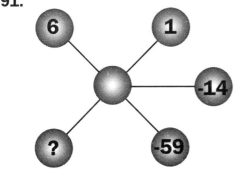

92.

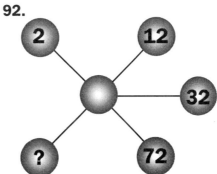

93.

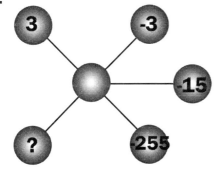

94.

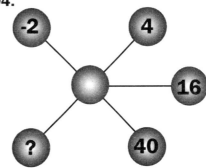

Answers on page 184

THE NUMBER STRADDLE

95.
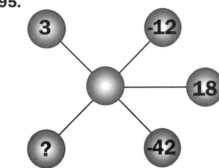

96.
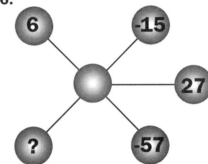

97.
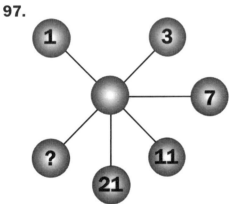

98.
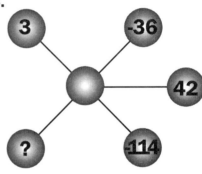

99.
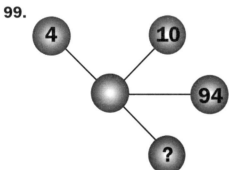

100.
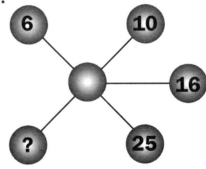

Answers on page 184

OBSTACLE 18 Select a route that takes you from the top number to the bottom number, which always follows a track downwards.

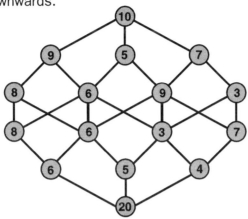

101. Can you find a route that gives you a sum of 49?
102. Can you find a route that gives you a total of 54?
103. What is the highest route value possible?
104. What is the lowest route value possible?
105. How many ways are there to have a route value of 57?

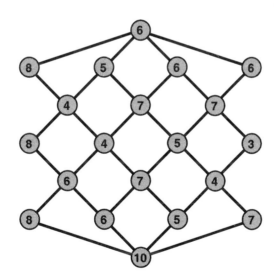

106. Can you find a route which gives you a total of 50?
107. What is the lowest possible route value?
108. What is the second highest route value?
109. How many routes give a value of 43?
110. Can you find a route to give a route value of 49?

Answers on page 184

OBSTACLE 19

111. A blacksmith had a surplus of horseshoes. He had bids from between 80 and 100 stables for the 1078 shoes. He wished to divide them equally. How many shoes did each stable get and how many stables were there?

112. My apple tree yielded a good load this year. I swapped half of the apples collected for other fruits and ate 4 apples myself. The next day I swapped half of the remaining apples for some wine and ate a further 3 apples. The next day I ate one apple and gave half of the remaining apples to friends. This left me with 5 apples. How many did I have to start with?

113. The minute hand on your clock is 7 cms long. If the point of the minute hand has travelled 14 cms, how much time has elapsed to the nearest second?

OBSTACLE 20 In the grid below the intersections have a value equal to the sum of the 4 adjacent numbers.

	A	B	C	D	E	F	G	
1	17	34	20	23	21	19	27	25
2	21	23	22	24	21	32	26	24
3	18	27	19	27	30	26	19	17
4	26	35	19	21	25	18	26	22
5	19	21	24	19	16	28	28	21
6	24	27	17	29	17	29	18	26
7	23	25	22	32	20	26	27	22
	27	18	20	23	24	29	20	22

114. Can you find two of the four intersections that have values of 100?
115. Which intersections have the lowest value?
116. What is the highest intersection value?
117. What is the highest intersection value on row 7?
118. What is the lowest intersection value on column B?
119. Which row or column has the most intersection values at 100 or more?
120. Which row or column of intersections has the lowest total value?

OBSTACLE 21

121. What day of the week has an alphabetical value of 100, if A=1, B=2, and Z=26, when all of the letter values are added together?

122. Dave had $5 plus one half of what Mary had. Mary had 40% of what Dave had. How much did Dave have?

OBSTACLE 22 What numbers should replace the question marks?

123.

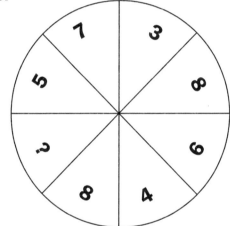

124.

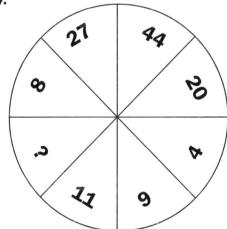

125.

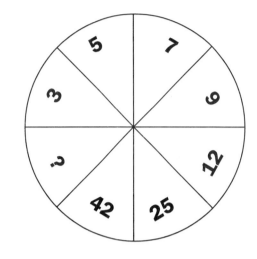

126.

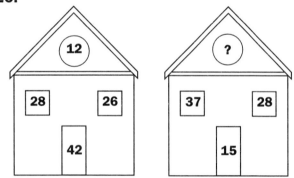

127.

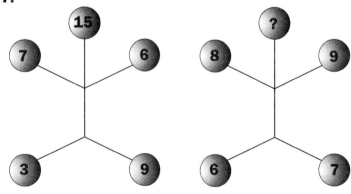

128.

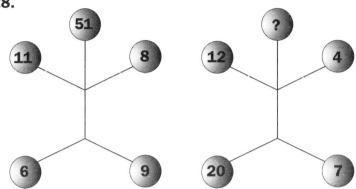

OBSTACLE 23

129. If FACE – DIED = – 67, what does HIDE – BEAD equal?

130. What number is missing from this sequence:

        2.5   4   5   10   25   ?

131. One man can dig a hole in 4 hours. A second man could dig the same hole in 5 hours. A third man could dig the same hole in 6 hours, and a fourth man could dig the same hole in 7 hours. If all of the men worked together to dig the hole, how long would it take to dig to the nearest minute?

132. Which number completes this sequence:

        7   49   441   ?

133. What number completes the sum below?

	D	A	M			A	I	L
+	8	8	7		+	?	?	?
	L	I	T			G	O	T

THE NUMBER STRADDLE

134. In 20 years' time Mrs Pye will be twice as old as her son. At the present time she is 7 times as old as her son. How old will she be in 15 years' time?

135. If SHELL = 77345 what number represents HOLES?

OBSTACLE 24   Using all of the outer circled numbers once only, can you find the missing numbers in the following questions?

136.

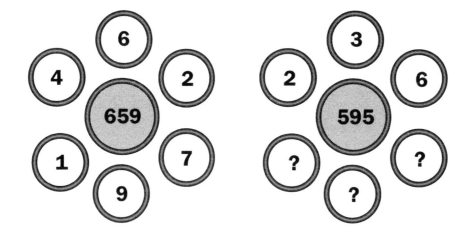

137.

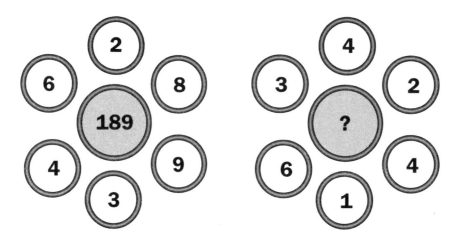

138.

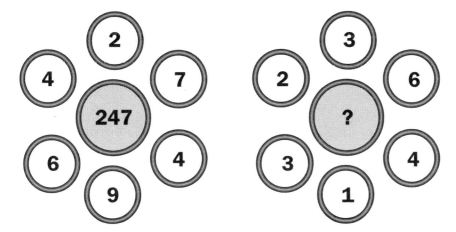

139.

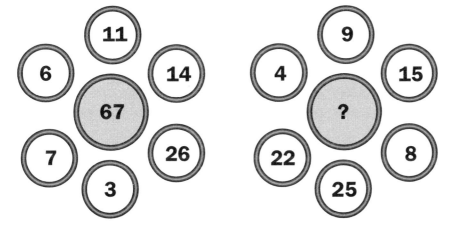

140.

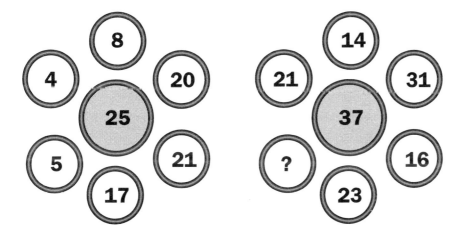

Answers on page 186

OBSTACLE 25 Calculate the values of the black, white, and shaded circles and the sum of the final set in each question.

141.

11   10   6   ?

142.

11   12   6   ?

143.

14   9   12   ?

144.

14   13   12   ?

145.

17   22   20   ?

146.

147.

148.

149.

150.

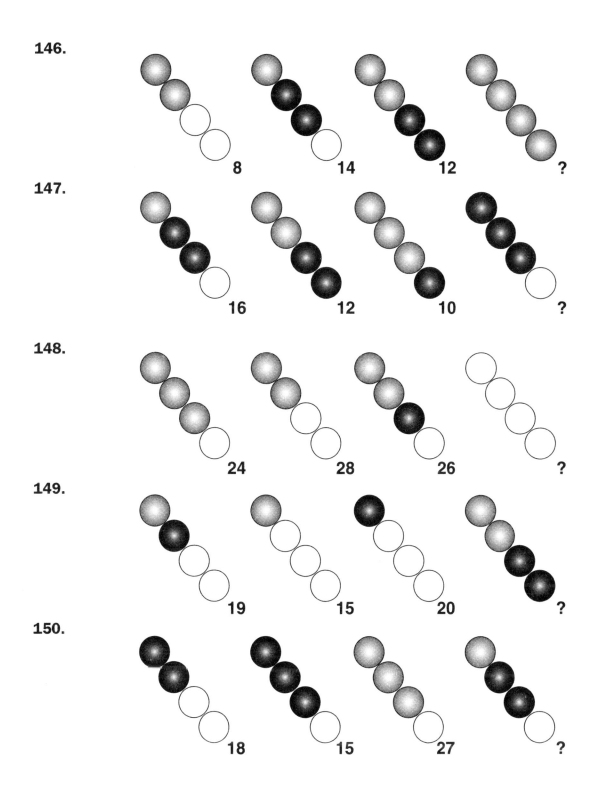

ZONE ⑦

ANSWERS

OBSTACLE 1

1. C.

2. E.

3. D.

4. B and C.

5. C.

6. Nobody.

OBSTACLE 2

7. 58.

8. 102.

9. 342.

10. 416.

OBSTACLE 3

11. 3.87. 116 passes for 30 students.

12. 3.32. 83 passes for 25 students.

13. 58.

OBSTACLE 4

14. 42. ★ = 17   ● = 5   ■ = 15

OBSTACLE 5

15. 500, 1000. Two methods. Either consecutive Roman numerals or an alternating series, x 5, x 2.

16. 203. Two methods. Either multiply previous number by 3 and deduct 1, or + 5, + 15, + 45, + 135.

17. 603. (previous + 3) x 3.

18. 6, 3, 2. Numbers 1 to 9 in alphabetic order.

19. 190. (+ 1 (x 2).

20. 41. Two methods. $5 + 1^2$, $5 + 2^2$, $5 + 3^2$, or series + 3, + 5, + 7, etc.

OBSTACLE 6

21. 328. Along each row multiply first two digits of first number to get first two digits of second number. Multiply last two digits of first number to get last two of second number and join them. 4 x 8 = 32, 2 x 4 = 8; 328.

22. 4752. In each number the first two digits are multiplied by the last two digits to give the next number along the row. 54 x 88 = 4752.

23. 184. In each row the two outer digits of the first number are multiplied to give the two outer digits of the second number. The two middle of the first number are multiplied to give the middle digits of the second number. 7 x 2 =14; 4 x 2 = 8; 184.

OBSTACLE 7

24. 3. (A + B) x C = D + E.

25. 3. (A + C) – (D x E) = B or A – B + C ÷ D = E.

26. 0 and 6. B + D = E ; E – A = C.

OBSTACLE 8

27. 3 white circles. Black circle values are: Top = 1, right = 2, bottom = 3, left = 4. Values are then added. White circle = 5. Sums are (1 + 3) x (4 + 1) = 20. (4 + 1) x (1 + 2) = 15. (4 + 1) + (2 + 3) = 10. (3 + 4 + 1) – (1 + 2) = 5.

28. 15 circles: Z = 5W, 3W = circle.

29. 6 circles. ★ = 3, n = 1½, ◯ = 2.

OBSTACLE 9

30. 1625. Add times as numbers. 135 + 600 = 735; 245 + 1215 = 1460;
520 + 1105 = 1625.

31. 294. Add numbers on pointers and complete the sum. (6 + 9) [15] x (1 + 6) [7] = 105;
(6 + 3) [9] x (9 + 3) [12] = 108; (12 + 9) [21] x (2 + 12) [14] = 294.

32. 1560. Add times as numbers. 200 + 730 = 930; 245 + 445 = 690;
915 + 645 = 1560.

33. 32. Multiply the hands by their sector values and complete the sum. (1 x 2) [2] +
(3 x 4) [12] = 14; (3 x 3) [9] + (2 x 2) [4] = 13; (4 x 4) [16] x (1 x 2) [2] = 32.

OBSTACLE 10

34.

18	6	4	30	47	29
45	30	6	18	17	2
1	21	1	42	23	5
3	28	7	17	1	6
44	4	32	43	30	40

35.

6	2	3	4	4	3
3	5	5	2	6	2
5	3	1	3	5	0
2	4	5	3	0	5
3	3	4	6	6	5

OBSTACLE 11

36.

3	6	3	4	4	6
4	4	7	2	8	3
5	8	5	5	6	7
6	5	3	7	8	2
8	3	1	6	5	4
2	7	8	7	5	3

37.

3	6	4	4	8	6
9	6	6	7	9	2
5	6	5	6	2	7
7	6	7	5	9	3
8	9	4	8	9	7
4	9	6	8	4	6

OBSTACLE 12

38. 4.The two-digit number on the left minus the two-digit number on the right gives the middle number.

39. 4.The two-digit number on the right minus the two-digit number on the left gives the middle number.

40. 6.The two-digit number on the left minus the two-digit number on the right gives the middle number.

41. 2.The two-digit number on the right minus the two-digit number on the left gives the middle number.

OBSTACLE 13

42. Add the two digits of each number together to give the number of places the numbers move round.

	34	
21		14
	55	

43. Add one to each number to give the amount of places each number moves around.

3		4
5		2

44. The difference between the two digits in each number gives the amount of places each number moves round.

	52	
41		48
	19	

Answers

OBSTACLE 14

45. Eleven. The values are totalled in each grid to give the number shown. The sum of the values of triangles and circles gives the answer. Δ = 2, O = 1.

46. −15. The sum of the values of white and black squares gives the answer.

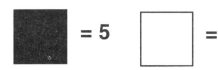

■ = 5   □ = −5

47. 22. The grid values are shown and the sum of the positions gives the answer.

4	3	2	1
5	6	7	8
12	11	10	9
13	14	15	16

OBSTACLE 15

48. Asterisk = 8, triangle = 12, square = 16, rectangle = 20.
49. 46.
50. 46.
51. 36.
52. 3. E2, E3, E4.

	A	B	C	D	E
1	8	8	14	10	6
2	26	✱	38	24	20
3	36	50	46	△	20
4	▬	46	■	32	20
5	28	42	34	22	14

53. Square = 10, asterisk = 18, triangle = 24.
54. 57.
55. 81.
56. 42.
57. 94, C4.
58. 318.

	A	B	C	D	E	F
1	19	31	31	26	12	12
2	28	■	57	43	29	17
3	37	★	78	△	46	22
4	53	77	94	81	■	22
5	39	★	△	64	34	22
6	30	42	47	38	17	5

OBSTACLE 16

59. David has $20, Mary has $4.
60. (2 + 6) divided by (7 − 4) x 9 = 24.
61. ¼. √64 = 8, so ¼ is to 4 as ⅛ is to 8.
62. 718.
63. 136.
64. 171.43 miles.
65. 235.72 miles.
66. 36 miles. Add alphabetical positional values of first and last letters.
67. 10, 11, 12.
68. 1, 6, 8.
69. 10. Alphabet values of the first letters of the months.
70. A = 4, B = 9, C = 5.
71. 56.
72. 64.
73. 100.
74. 144.
75. 1.
76. 45.
77. 30.
78. 8.8.
79. 181.02.
80. 34.

THE NUMBER STRADDLE

Answers

OBSTACLE 17   In the next 20 answers, n = previous number.

81.	$-26. (n \times 2) - 6.$		**82.**	$83. (n \times 3) - 4.$
83.	$834. n^2 - 7.$		**84.**	$122. (n + 3) \times 2.$
85.	$132. (n - 7) \times 3.$		**86.**	$19. 2n - 3.$
87.	$-337. 4n - 13.$		**88.**	$402. 3 (2 + n).$
89.	$163. (n \times 3) - 2.$		**90.**	$246. 3n - 6.$
91.	$-194. 3n - 17.$		**92.**	$152. 2(n + 4).$
93.	$-65535. 2n - n^2.$		**94.**	$88. 2n + 8.$
95.	$78. -2(n + 3).$		**96.**	$111. (-2n) - 3$
97.	39. Add previous 3 numbers.		**98.**	$198. -2(n + 15).$
99.	$8830. n^2 - 6.$		**100.**	$38\frac{1}{2}. (1\frac{1}{2}n) + 1.$

OBSTACLE 18

101.   10—5—6—3—5—20.

102.   10—7—9—3—5—20.

103.   61: 10—9—8—8—6—20.

104.   47: 10—7—3—3—4—20.

105.   3 ways

       10—9—6—6—6—20.

       10—7—9—7—4—20.

       10—7—9—6—5—20.

106.   6—8—4—8—6—8—10.

107.   41 (4 ways).

       6—5—4—4—6—6—10

       6—5—4—4—7—5—10

       6—6(rc)—7—3—4—5—10

       6—6(r)—7—3—4—5—10

108.   48: 6—8—4—8—6—6—10.

109.   6 routes.

       6—5—4—4—6—8—10.

       6—6—7—5—4—5—10.

       6—6—7—5—4—5—10.

       6—6—7—3—4—7—10.

       6—6—7—5—4—5—10.

       6—6—7—3—4—7—10.

110.   No route gives this total.

OBSTACLE 19

111. 11 horseshoes each for 98 stables.
112. 64.
113. 19 minutes 6 seconds.

OBSTACLE 20

114. There are 4: B3, F4, C6, F6.
115. D4 and D5. Both have 81.
116. E2. 109.
117. F. 102.
118. 7. 85.
119. Col F. 6.
120. Col C and Row 5. Both add up to 636.

OBSTACLE 21

121. Wednesday.
122. Dave had $6.25 (Mary had $2.50).

OBSTACLE 22

123. 3. Sum of diagonally opposite segments equals 11.
124. 4. Reading clockwise, the lower half numbers are multiplied by 2, 3, 4, 5, respectively to equal diagonally opposite upper sector.
125. 63. Reading clockwise, the upper half numbers are multiplied by 4, 5, 6, 7, respectively to equal diagonally opposite lower sector.
126. 50. (Window + window) – door = roof. (37 + 28) [65] – 15 = 50.
127. 30. (Arm x arm) – (leg x leg) = head. (8 x 9) [72] – (6 x 7) [42] = 30.
128. 4. (Left arm x right left) – (right arm x left leg) = head. (12 x 7) [84] – (4 x 20) [80] = 4.

ZONE ⑦

OBSTACLE 23

129. 140. The alpha positions squared of each letter are added and the sum then completed. The sum for FACE – DIED is $(6^2 + 1^2 + 3^2 + 5^2)$ [71] – $(4^2 + 9^2 + 5^2 + 4^2)$ [138] = –67; for HIDE – BEAD is $(8^2 + 9^2 + 4^2 + 5^2)$ [186] – $(2^2 + 5^2 + 1^2 + 4^2)$ [46] = 140.

130. 125. Multiply the previous two numbers and divide by 2.

131. 79 minutes. (1 hour 19 minutes).

132. 441. Multiply last term in each number by the number. (7 x 7), (9 x 49), (441 x 1).

133. 668. Alpha numeric sum. AIL (1, 9, 12) + 6, 6, 8 = 7 (G), 15 (O), 20 (T).

134. 43 years old. She is currently 28 and her son is 4.

135. 53704 (calculator display shown upside-down).

OBSTACLE 24

136. 359. Top number + lower number = middle number. 462 + 197 = 659.

137. –272. Top number – lower number = middle number.

138. 88. Sum of top 3 numbers x sum of bottom 3 numbers = middle number.

139. 83. Sum of all numbers in outer circles.

140. 6. Sum of diagonally opposite numbers is middle number.

OBSTACLE 25

141. 8. Black = 2; white = 1; shaded = 3.

142. 8. Black = 2; white = 1; shaded = 4.

143. 10. Black = 1; white = 4; shaded = 3.

144. 12. Black = 3; white = 4; shaded = 2.

145. 13. Black = 4; white = 7; shaded = 2.

146. 4. Black = 5; white = 3; shaded = 1.

147. 18. Black = 4; white = 6; shaded = 2.

148. 36. Black = 7; white = 9; shaded = 5.

149. 22. Black = 8; white = 4; shaded = 3.

150. 19. Black = 3; white = 6; shaded = 7.

SCORING SYSTEM

Now only the very best will survive

Promotion Criteria (See page 21):

Under 70	Busted two ranks.
71 - 80	Busted one rank.
81 - 100	No progress.
101 - 120	Promoted one rank.
121 +	Promoted two ranks.

AGE BONUS CHART

AGE IN YEARS	10	10.5	11	11.5	12	12.5	13	13.5	14	14.5	15	15.5
BONUS POINTS	40	35	30	25	20	18	16	14	12	10	8	4

ZONE ⑧

THE WORD CLAMBER

At least 145 more word conundrums, and they are even more of a struggle !

OBSTACLE 1 Which word is closest in meaning to the given word? Is it A, B, C, D, or E?

		A	B	C	D	E
1.	FLAIR	Fashionable	Talent	Style	Able	Quality
2.	BONA-FIDE	Correct	Factual	Genuine	Real	Precise
3.	ARID	Cold	Desolate	Deserted	Dry	Burnt
4.	BOISTEROUS	Carefree	Excessive	Unruly	Evil	Devilish
5.	ENDOW	Testament	Probate	Bequeath	Payment	Insurance
6.	PUNY	Petite	Minute	Weak	Soft	Simple
7.	DEMEAN	Arguable	Cheat	Defraud	Degrade	Libel
8.	ATTEST	Protect	Save	Vouch	Warrant	Defend
9.	MEDITATE	Wonder	Consult	Ruminate	Trance	Rest
10.	FLABBY	Soft	Elastic	Unctuous	Waxy	Flaccid
11.	WILD	Feral	Fierce	Violent	Temperamental	Rural
12.	ACRID	Sharp	Nasty	Tart	Bad-tempered	Pungent
13.	MERGE	Coalition	Fusion	Union	Combine	Incorporate
14.	STABLE	Constant	Durable	Permanent	Static	Unalterable
15.	RAPID	Brisk	Fast	Flying	Hasty	Prompt
16.	GOODWILL	Benevolent	Kindliness	Generous	Zealous	Virtue
17.	IMPLORE	Ask	Begged	Plead	Force	Solicit
18.	DORMANT	Asleep	Comatose	Hibernating	Inactive	Latent
19.	OPACITY	Cloudiness	Dullness	Obscurity	Transparent	Unclear
20.	UPKEEP	Aid	Maintenance	Preserve	Conserve	Promote

Answers on page 196

OBSTACLE 2   Rearrange each group of letters to form three words using all of the letters.

21.	D	E	E	I	R	S	V
22.	E	I	L	M	S		
23.	A	D	E	L	S	T	
24.	A	B	E	D	R		
25.	E	O	R	R	S	T	
26.	A	D	E	G	N	R	
27.	A	C	E	P	R	S	
28.	A	C	E	N	R	T	
29.	A	C	G	I	N	O	S	T
30.	A	G	I	N	P	R	S
31.	A	C	E	L	R	T	
32.	A	C	G	I	N	R	
33.	E	O	Q	R	T	U	
34.	I	N	O	P	S	T	
35.	I	L	O	P	S	T	
36.	E	G	I	N	S	T	W
37.	A	E	E	L	M	S	S	T
38.	E	E	K	L	S		
39.	D	E	I	N	N	T	
40.	A	E	E	G	L	N	R

OBSTACLE 3   In each of the following groups of words there is a hidden common connection. Can you identify the connection?

41.	IMPORTED	COLANDER	FORSAKE	ANTEATER
42.	MINUTES	SELFISHNESS	TRIBUNAL	SHOWPIECE
43.	EXPANSE	RADISH	MUTINY	DEPOT
44.	ENTWINE	MASSAGE	CRUSTATION	KEROSENE
45.	ROMANTIC	GRUFFLY	MOTHER	BEEFBURGER
46.	TRACTOR	DOVETAIL	CRISPY	STATUTORY
47.	BRANCH	UNICORN	WAISTCOATS	AVARICE
48.	ACCENT	DIMENSION	BRANDISH	HYENA
49.	CLIMATE	BARITONE	NICEST	CORKAGE
50.	TUSSOCK	ADDRESS	SHATTERED	COATING

Answers on pages 196 & 197

OBSTACLE 4   What, or where am I?

51. My first is in FIRE but not in GRATE
My second is in EARLY but not in LATE
My third is in MUSIC and also in TUNE
My fourth is in DISTINCT but not in SOON
My last is in FROST and also in SLEET
When ripe, I am juicy and sweet.
What am I?

52. My first is in LAMP but not in LIGHT
My second is in MAY but not in MIGHT
My third is in DART and also in BOARD
My fourth is in STRING but not in CORD
My last is in SEE but not in GLANCE
I am a city renowned for romance.
Where am I?

53. My first is in ACT but not in PLAY
My second is in APRIL but not in MAY
My third is in NOBLE and also in LORD
My fourth is in CARD but not in BOARD
My last is in STACK but not in HAY
You look at me every single day.
What am I?

54. My first is in PASS but not in FAIL
My second is in SHOP but not in SALE
My third is in HAIR and also in FACE
My fourth is in CARRY but not in CASE
My last is in ASK but not in PLEA
You wouldn't want to swim with me.
What am I?

55. My first is in CASH and also in CHEQUE
My second is in COLLAR but not in NECK
My third is in FINGER and also in RING
My fourth is in SONG but not in SING
My last is in WATER but not in MOAT
I am a narrow paddle boat.
What am I?

56. My first is in JUNE and also in JULY
My second is in CLEVER but not in SLY
My third is in PLANT and also in FLOWER
My fourth is in MUSCLE but not in POWER
My last is in GLOOMY but not in MOOD
My whole is a brightly coloured food.
What am I?

57. My first is in HOT and also in COLD
My second is in BRASH but not in BOLD
My third is in GANG and also in GROUP
My fourth is in ARMY but not in TROOP
My last is in LOAN and also in RENT
I am a musical instrument.
What am I?

58. My first is in MOCK but not in FAKE
My second is in BOIL but not in BAKE
My third is in ROCK and also in ROLL
My fourth is in WINDOW but not in POLE
My last is in BASIN but not in BATH
I do tricks to make children laugh.
What am I?

Answers on page 197

59. My first is in SPRING but not in SUMMER
My second is in BAND but not in DRUMMER
My third is in ORANGE and also in RED
My fourth is in TALK but not in SAID
My last is in FROSTY but not in SNOW
I am a fun place to go.
What am I?

60. My first is in SPRINT but not in RUN
My second is in BREAD but not in BUN
My third is in TALL and also in SHORT
My fourth is in BOAT but not in PORT
My last is in STEEPLE but not in TOWER
I am a delicate part of a flower.
What am I?

OBSTACLE 5

61. There have been orders for 200 Rolls Royces, 115 Vauxhalls, and 500 Hondas. How many orders have there been for Renaults?

62. Donna has won 500 dance competitions, Patricia has won 102, and Charlotte has won 150. How many competitions has Louise won?

63 A model shop has ordered 100 kits of cars, 1000 monster kits, and 600 doll kits. How many space-rocket kits did they order?

64. In a studio audience 8 of the guests are from Virginia, 56 are from Pennsylvania, 1 is from Arizona, and 10 are from Texas. How many guests are there from New Mexico?

65. A price list in a London pottery and china store shows the price of a cup in its various departments. How much should a Wedgewood cup cost?

Royal Doulton	**£6.00**
Denby	**£5.00**
Royal Worcester	**£1.50**
Wedgewood	**£?**

THE WORD CLAMBER

ZONE ⑧

OBSTACLE 6 When each of the following words is rearranged, one group of letters can be used as a prefix for the others to form longer words. Which is the prefix and what does it become?

	A	B	C	D	E
66.	LET	BUS	MILE	RUB	DENT
67.	CHAR	MATS	DIES	NIPS	OPT
68.	SHINES	HIRE	DIE	TIP	SON
69.	EAT	SET	LAP	TAPE	TAME
70.	NIP	LIES	ANT	NOD	NET
71.	TESS	SHIN	LAID	NOTE	ROC
72.	STEM	SINES	RAW	SEND	MITE
73.	BALE	DICE	NIGH	TON	RAY
74.	LEST	SUB	TIES	GINS	DIE
75.	HAS	NET	TOP	OAT	GATE

OBSTACLE 7 Rearrange the following to form five connected words. What are they?

76.	ZAMAD	NERTOIC	GUPEETO	TRULEAN	SHIMSTIBUI
77.	NIGEAU	KEELSH	TEESAP	COCKEP	ODESUC
78.	CUGIC	AGEREJ	DINOM	LENCAH	DIDLELOF
79.	TAJECK	HIRST	PRUMEJ	STRUSORE	HOSES
80.	MONZAA	GEANGS	SMATHE	TAZEGYN	BAZZEMI
81.	TALAM	CRIPA	ZAIBI	CYLISI	SHEDOR
82.	BREANCAR	SLEBURSS	SONLIB	RADDIM	TOPRIERA
83.	DAZBUZR	CLOFNA	GEALE	TULRUVE	KHAW
84.	MANDOTBIN	SABBELLA	SKATBEALLB	GOXNIB	COHYEK
85.	STOBERL	WRANP	ROTUT	SMOLAN	CLAIPE

192

Answers on page 198

OBSTACLE 8 Add the vowels in the following groups of letters to form five words, one of which does not belong with the others. Which word is the odd one out?

	A	B	C	D	E
86.	WLKG	JGGNG	RNNNG	SPRNTNG	STTNG
87.	MSM	MSQ	TMPL	CTHDRL	SYNGG
88.	NSHVLL	SVNNH	LNDN	DTRT	DNVR
89.	MNDY	WDNSDY	JNRY	SNDY	STRDY
90.	RD	YLLW	CRCL	CRMSN	PRPL
91.	ND	TLY	KNY	DLLS	CLND
92.	NGN	CLTCH	GRS	WHLS	LMN
93.	TWNTY	KYBRD	SCRN	MMRY	PRCSSR
94.	CRPHLLY	GRGNZL	STLTN	BR	BLGNS
95.	PLM	PTT	STSM	PRCT	DMSN

OBSTACLE 9 Join the letters of the given words to form a single word using all of the letters.

96.	DRUM	+	MIMES			
97.	REPAY	+	LIT	+	SON	
98.	DANCE	+	SIT			
99.	SPITE	+	ANTIC			
100.	MEAN	+	ATE			
101.	MONSTER	+	RATE			
102.	CLEMENT	+	RAPE			
103.	DEAD	+	CITE			
104.	NIECE	+	GILL	+	NET	
105.	SHINE	+	SUIT	+	CAT	

OBSTACLE 10 In each of the questions below, 3 pairs of words are given. Match the pair to form 3 longer words.

106.	MAIDEN	VENDOR	HAND	MASTER	NEWS	SHIP
107.	MAN	PAWN	MASTER	LIVERY	PAY	BROKER
108.	SHOOTER	HOUSE	WRITER	SHARP	MASTER	SIGN
109.	PLAY	REEL	NEWS	SCREEN	LIGHT	FOOT
110.	EVER	DAY	DOMES	WHEN	TAIL	WHITE
111.	SPUR	DROP	LILY	LARK	WATER	SNOW
112.	LESS	EARTH	LIST	SACK	QUAKE	RAN
113.	RAM	PEACE	WORD	PART	PASS	ABLE
114.	CRACK	AGE	FOR	BLOCK	WISE	WARD
115.	NAP	HOOD	KID	SOME	FALSE	TROUBLE
116.	MAKER	BOY	LOCK	FRIEND	PEACE	DEAD
117.	TOP	SET	FREE	CARE	MOST	BACK
118.	WHOLE	WIRE	HAY	BAT	SALE	TEN
119.	NECK	ABLE	EYE	BOTTLE	BREAK	SORE
120.	LOVED	GOOD	WILD	BE	LIFE	WILL
121.	SOME	HARDY	FOOL	RAGE	HAND	BAR
122.	ION	AND	LEDGE	REFLECT	KNOW	BRIG
123.	CON	WORK	SIGN	GUESS	POST	TRIBUTE
124.	AGE	HOD	BOND	MAN	SHOW	SLIPS
125.	OUR	FALL	TEN	ROT	RUM	WIND

Answers on page 200

OBSTACLE 11 For each word shown write another word with the same meaning beginning with the letter G.

126.	COLLECT	_ _ _ _ _ _
127.	HEREDITARY	_ _ _ _ _ _ _
128.	PERMIT	_ _ _ _ _
129.	DISTRESS	_ _ _ _ _
130.	ELEGANCE	_ _ _ _ _
131.	WOLVERINE	_ _ _ _ _ _ _
132.	STUCK	_ _ _ _ _
133.	INORDINATE	_ _ _ _ _
134.	LAMENT	_ _ _ _ _ _
135.	OPENING	_ _ _
136.	PLEASE	_ _ _ _ _ _ _
137.	RAPT	_ _ _ _ _ _ _
138.	BLUSTERY	_ _ _ _ _
139.	STOCK	_ _ _ _ _
140.	STOMACH	_ _ _
141.	WILDEBEEST	_ _ _
142.	TRICKERY	_ _ _ _ _
143.	HAMMER	_ _ _ _ _
144.	CARGO	_ _ _ _ _
145.	RELIGIOUS	_ _ _ _ _

Answers on Page 200

ZONE 8

ANSWERS

OBSTACLE 1

1.	B. Talent.	**2.**	C. Genuine.
3.	D. Dry.	**4.**	C. Unruly.
5.	C. Bequeath.	**6.**	C. Weak.
7.	D. Degrade.	**8.**	C. Vouch.
9.	C. Ruminate.	**10.**	E. Flaccid.
11.	A. Feral.	**12.**	E. Pungent.
13.	D. Combine.	**14.**	A. Constant.
15.	B. Fast.	**16.**	B. Kindliness.
17.	C. Plead.	**18.**	D. Inactive.
19.	D. Obscurity	**20.**	B. Maintenance.

OBSTACLE 2

21. Derives, Diverse, Revised.

22. Limes, Miles, Slime, Smile.

23. Deltas, Lasted, Salted, Slated.

24. Bared, Beard, Bread, Debar.

25. Resort, Roster, Sorter, Storer.

26. Danger, Gander, Garden, Ranged.

27. Capers, Pacers, Parsec, Recaps, Scrape.

28. Canter, Carnet, Nectar, Recant, Trance.

29. Coasting, Agnostic, Coatings.

30. Parings, Parsing, Rasping, Sparing.

31. Claret, Cartel, Rectal.

32. Arcing, Caring, Racing.

33. Quoter, Roquet, Torque.
34. Pintos, Piston, Pitons, Points.
35. Pilots, Pistol, Postil, Spoilt.
36. Stewing, Twinges, Westing.
37. Mateless, Meatless, Tameless.
38. Keels, Leeks, Sleek.
39. Indent, Intend, Tinned.
40. Enlarge, General, Gleaner.

OBSTACLE 3

41. Port, Cola, Sake, Tea.
42. Nut, Fish, Bun, Pie.
43. Pan, Dish, Tin, Pot.
44. Wine, Sage, Rust, Rose.
45. Ant, Fly, Moth, Bee.
46. Actor, Vet, Spy, Tutor.
47. Bran, Corn, Oats, Rice.
48. Cent, Dime, Rand, Yen.
49. Lima, Bari, Nice, Cork.
50. Sock, Dress, Hat, Coat.

OBSTACLE 4

51. Fruit.
52. Paris.
53. Clock.
54. Shark.
55. Canoe.
56. Jelly.
57. Organ.
58. Clown.
59. Party.
60. Petal.

OBSTACLE 5

61. 50. Letters that are Roman numerals in the names are added together.
62. 51. Letters that are Roman numerals in the names are added together.
63. 200. Letters that are Roman numerals in the names are added together.
64. 1111. Letters that are Roman numerals in the names are added together.
65. £10.00. Letters that are Roman numerals in the names are added together.

OBSTACLE 6

66. B. SUB. Subtle, Sublime, Suburb, Subtend.
67. E. TOP. Toparch, Topmast, Topside, Topspin.
68. D. PIT. Pithiness, Pithier, Pitied, Pitons.
69. C. PAL. Palate, Palest, Palpate, Palmate.
70. E. TEN. Tenant, Tenpin, Tendon, Tensile.
71. E. COR. Cordial, Coronet, Cornish, Corsets.
72. C. WAR. Wardens, Wartime, Warmest, Wariness.
73. D. NOT. Nothing, Notary, Notable, Noticed.
74. B. BUS. Busiest, Bussing, Bustles, Busied.
75. C. POT. Pottage, Potash, Potent, Potato.

OBSTACLE 7

76. Mazda, Citroen, Peugeot, Renault, Mitsubishi.
77. Guinea, Shekel, Peseta, Copeck, Escudo.
78. Gucci, Jaeger, Mondi, Chanel, Oldfield.
79. Jacket, Shirt, Jumper, Trousers, Shoes.
80. Amazon, Ganges, Thames, Yangtze, Zambezi.
81. Malta, Capri, Ibiza, Sicily, Rhodes.
82. Canberra, Brussels, Lisbon, Madrid, Pretoria.
83. Buzzard, Falcon, Eagle, Vulture, Hawk.
84. Badminton, Baseball, Basketball, Boxing, Hockey.
85. Lobster, Prawn, Trout, Salmon, Plaice.

OBSTACLE 8

86. E. Sitting. The others are Walking, Jogging, Running, Sprinting.
87. A. Museum. The others are Mosque, Temple, Cathedral, Synagogue.
88. C. London. The others are cities in the USA; Nashville, Savannah, Detroit, Denver.
89. C. January. The others are days of the week; Monday, Wednesday, Sunday, Saturday.
90. C. Circle. The others are colors; Red, Yellow, Crimson, Purple.
91. D. Dallas. The others are India, Italy, Kenya, Iceland.
92. E. Lemon. The others are car parts; Engine, Clutch, Gears, Wheels.
93. A. Twenty. The others are computer parts; Keyboard, Screen, Memory, Processor.
94. E. Bolognese. The others are Caerphilly, Gorgonzola, Stilton, Brie.
95. B. Potato. The others are Plum, Satsuma, Apricot, Damson.

OBSTACLE 9

96. Midsummer.
97. Personality.
98. Distance.
99. Antiseptic.
100. Emanate.
101. Remonstrate.
102. Replacement.
103. Dedicate.
104. Intelligence.
105. Enthusiastic.

ZONE ⑧

OBSTACLE 10

106. Handmaiden, Newsvendor, Shipmaster.
107. Liveryman, Paymaster, Pawnbroker.
108. Signwriter, Sharpshooter, Housemaster.
109. Screenplay, Newsreel, Footlight.
110. Whenever, Domesday, Whitetail.
111. Larkspur, Snowdrop, Waterlily.
112. Listless, Earthquake, Ransack.
113. Rampart, Password, Peaceable.
114. Wisecrack, Blockage, Forward.
115. Kidnap, Falsehood, Troublesome.
116. Deadlock, Peacemaker, Boyfriend.
117. Setback, Topmost, Carefree.
118. Wholesale, Batten, Haywire.
119. Eyesore, Breakable, Bottleneck.
120. Beloved, Wildlife, Goodwill.
121. Handsome, Foolhardy, Barrage.
122. Reflection, Brigand, Knowledge.
123. Contribute, Signpost, Guesswork.
124. Bondage, Slipshod, Showman.
125. Windfall, Rotten, Rumour.

OBSTACLE 11

126. Gather.
127. Genetic.
128. Grant.
129. Grief.
130. Grace.
131. Glutton.
132. Glued.
133. Great.
134. Grieve.
135. Gap.
136. Gratify.
137. Gripped.
138. Gusty.
139. Goods.
140. Gut.
141. Gnu.
142. Guile.
143. Gavel.
144. Goods.
145. Godly.

SCORING SYSTEM

Is it time for you to take an early pension?

Promotion Criteria (See page 21):

Under 80	*"Have you given up yet?"* Demoted one rank.
81 – 100	No progress.
101 – 130	Promoted one rank.
131 +	Promoted two ranks.

AGE BONUS POINTS

AGE IN YEARS	10	10.5	11	11.5	12	12.5	13	13.5	14	14.5	15	15.5
BONUS POINTS	35	30	27	25	22	20	18	16	14	10	7	4

ZONE ⑨

More information to memorize and more questions to answer, but no more time to do them in. Stretch those brain cells!

MEMORY TEST 1

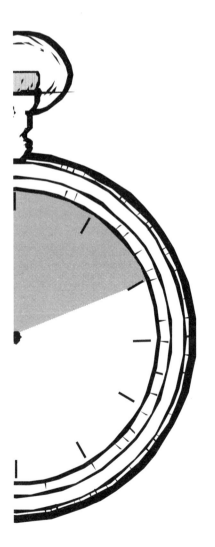

Study the grid on the next page for 2 minutes, then begin the test on the page after.

ONCE THE TEST HAS STARTED YOU
MUST NOT LOOK BACK

Set the clock and begin

Time allowed for this test
10 MINUTES

	A	B	C	D	E	F
1						
2						
3	4	9	7	3	0	2
4						
5	D	L	G	M	Z	K
6						

ZONE 9

1. Reading from the left, what number came after number 7?

2. What was the fifth object in the fourth row?

3. How many men were shown?

4. Where were the two birds located?

5. What items made of glass were in the first row?

6. What two letters followed D in the fifth row?

7. If you added the numbers in the third row, what would they total?

8. What item of furniture would you find in the second row column E?

9. What sport is the girl playing?

10. In which direction is the cartoon bird looking?

11. How many vowels were in the fifth row?

12. Were the scissor handles pointing up, down, to the left, or to the right?

13. How many balls were shown?

14. What is shown on position F2?

15. What numbers were at the ends of the third line?

16. What can be seen in the four middle boxes?

17. What was the fourth object on the first line?

18. What was the total number of legs in the bottom row?

19. What object is in the top right corner?

20. What is in box A4?

21. What object was two positions above the number 7?

22. What was the fifth object in the first line?

23. What is the grid reference of the sports car?

24. What letters were at each end of the fifth line?

25. What object was under the number 2?

26. In which direction was the bicycle pointing?

27. What do the contents of the third and fifth boxes in the first column have in common?

28. What letter was two places to the left of the letter Z?

29. What was the lowest number?

30. What was positioned three places above the letter M?

MORE MEMORY TESTS

1. ....
2. ....
3. ....
4. ....
5. ....
6. ....
7. ....
8. ....
9. ....
10. ....
11. ....
12. ....
13. ....
14. ....
15. ....
16. ....
17. ....
18. ....
19. ....
20. ....
21. ....
22. ....
23. ....
24. ....
25. ....
26. ....
27. ....
28. ....
29. ....
30. ....

Answers on page 230

MORE MEMORY TESTS

MEMORY TEST 2

Study the menu on the next page for 2 minutes, then begin the test on the page after.

ONCE THE TEST HAS STARTED YOU
MUST NOT LOOK BACK

Set the clock and begin

Time allowed for this test
10 MINUTES

INTERNATIONAL
MENU

INDIAN

Starter	Price (Rupees)
Samosa	1200
Pakora	1200
Shish Kebab	900

Main Course	
Chicken Masala	3000
Lamb Bhuna	3600
Chicken Vindaloo	3600
Chicken Korma	3000
Chicken Tandoori	3600
(Rice not included)	

Dessert	
Kulfi	1200
Banana Fritters	1800

ENGLISH

Starter	Price (Sterling)
Tomato Soup	2.00
Cock-A-Leekie Soup	2.00

Main Course	
Roast Beef and Yorkshire Pudding	6.00
Cottage Pie	4.00
Welsh Rarebit	4.00

Dessert	
Jam Roly Poly and Custard	2.00
Apple Pie and Cream	3.00

FRENCH

Starter	Price (Francs)
Snails	20
Frogs' Legs	20

Main Course	
Boeuf Bourguignon	60
Chateaubriand	80
Ratatouille	40

Dessert	
Crêpe Suzettes	30

ITALIAN

Starter	Price (Lire)
Minestrone Soup	2400

Main Course	
Spaghetti Bolognese	6000
Lasagna	6000
Pizza (Assorted toppings)	4800

Dessert	
Ice Cream	2400
Zabaglione	3600

Credit cards are not accepted.

1. There are four cuisines to choose from, what are they?
2. From the Indian menu how many main dishes of Chicken were there to choose from?
3. From the French menu, how many starters were there?
4. You had Spaghetti Bolognese from the Italian menu. How much did it cost?
5. Was the Chateaubriand cheaper than the Boeuf Bourguignon?
6. How much was Roast Beef and Yorkshire Pudding?
7. What was the name of the Lamb dish from the Indian menu?
8. How many desserts were on the English menu?
9. Were there more main courses on the French menu or the Italian menu?
10. What was the title of the Menu?
11. Which menu had Banana Fritters?
12. Which menus have soup as a starter?
13. Was there rice included with the Chicken Korma?
14. How much did the Crêpe Suzettes cost?
15. How much did the Cottage Pie cost?
16. How many soups were on the menu altogether?
17. Could you have assorted toppings on the Pizza?
18. What words were written along the bottom of the menu?
19. Can you name the two desserts on the Italian menu?
20. How many starters were there on the Indian menu?
21. There are two types of soup for starters on the English menu. What are they?
22. What is the cheapest starter on the Indian menu?
23. Which menu has the least choice of sweets?
24. You choose Frogs' Legs and Chateaubriand. How much is your bill?
25. How many main course dishes are there on the Indian menu?
26. What was the starter on the Italian menu?
27. You choose Ratatouille for your main course. Which menu are you choosing from?
28. How much would you pay for Tomato Soup and Cottage Pie from the English menu?
29. You choose Lasagna and Zabaglione. How much is your bill?
30. How much was the coffee on the French menu?

MORE MEMORY TESTS

1. ....

2. ....

3. ....

4. ....

5. ....

6. ....

7. ....

8. ....

9. ....

10. ....

11. ....

12. ....

13. ....

14. ....

15. ....

16. ....

17. ....

18. ....

19. ....

20. ....

21. ....

22. ....

23. ....

24. ....

25. ....

26. ....

27. ....

28. ....

29. ....

30. ....

Answers on page 230

MORE MEMORY TESTS

MEMORY TEST 3

Study the TV schedule on the next page for 2 minutes, then begin the test on the following page.

ONCE THE TEST HAS STARTED YOU
MUST NOT LOOK BACK

Set the clock and begin

Time allowed for this test
10 MINUTES

"TV GUIDE"

SATURDAY *19TH JULY 1996*

CHANNEL 1		CHANNEL 2		CHANNEL 3	
5.50	Baywatch	6.00	Movie: Lethal Weapon	5.15	Movie: Goldfinger
6.35	News	7.40	Sports Update	7.00	Football Preview
7.00	Friends	8.00	Movie: Pulp Fiction	7.45	News & Weather
7.45	Basketball	9.50	News	8.05	Movie: Speed 2
8.45	News	10.00	Movie: Sommersby	10.15	Movie: Dances
9.00	Movie: Top Gun	11.45	Movie: Pretty In Pink		With Wolves
				11.40	News

ZONE ⑨

1. How many channels are there?

2. What is the date of the TV Guide?

3. How many shows are there on Channel 3?

4. How many movies are showing on Channel 1?

5. What time is the first show on Channel 2?

6. What time is the movie *Speed 2* on?

7. How many movies are there altogether?

8. What movie would you be watching on Channel 2 at 10.00?

9. How many news shows are there on Channel 1?

10. What time is the first news show on Channel 1?

11. What is on at 7.40 on Channel 2?

12. What time is *Friends* on?

13. What time is the movie *Pretty In Pink* on?

14. Is *Goldfinger* on Channel 3 or Channel 2?

15. What time does *Sommersby* finish?

16. What time does the basketball start?

17. Is *Football Preview* shown on Channel 2?

18. How many news shows are there altogether?

19. What time does *Top Gun* start?

20. What time does *Pulp Fiction* finish?

MORE MEMORY TESTS

1. _____

2. _____

3. _____

4. _____

5. _____

6. _____

7. _____

8. _____

9. _____

10. _____

11. _____

12. _____

13. _____

14. _____

15. _____

16. _____

17. _____

18. _____

19. _____

20. _____

Answers on page 231

MEMORY TEST 4

Study the poem on the next page for 3 minutes, then begin the test on the following page.

ONCE THE TEST HAS STARTED YOU
MUST NOT LOOK BACK

Set the clock and begin

Time allowed for this test
10 MINUTES

NIGHT
By William Blake

The sun descending in the west,
The evening star does shine,
The birds are silent in their rest
And I must seek for mine
The moon, like a flower
In heaven's high tower
While silent delight
Sits and smiles on the night.

Farewell green fields and happy groves
Where flocks have took delight
Where lambs have nibbled silent moves
The feet of angels bright
Unseen they pour blessing
And joy without ceasing
On each bud and blossom
And each sleeping bosom.

They look in every thoughtless rest
Where birds are covered warm
They visit cares of every breast
To keep them all from harm
If they see any weeping
That should have been sleeping
They pour sleep on their head
And sit down by their bed.

When wolves and tygers howl for prey
They pitying stand and weep
Seeking to drive their thirst away
And keep them from the sheep
But if they rush dreadful
The angels most heedful
Receive each mild spirit
New worlds to inherit.

1. How many verses are there?

2. Where is the sun descending?

3. What is the first line of the first verse?

4. The birds are in their rest. What are they doing?

5. What is the moon described as?

6. What have nibbled?

7. Were the hands of angels bright or the feet of angels bright?

8. What animals howl for prey?

9. What is the last line of the last verse?

10. Were the birds warm or cold?

11. Complete this sentence;

    "They pour sleep on their head,

    And sit down by ? ?"

12. Were the wolves seeking to drive their hunger or thirst away?

13. The angels were seeking to drive the wolves' hunger/thirst away to keep them from what?

14. By receiving each mild spirit what was it hoped they would inherit?

15. Complete this line;

    "Farewell green fields and ? ?"

16. How many animals are mentioned in the poem?

17. Was the North Star or the Evening Star shining?

18. Who wrote the poem?

19. What was the poem called?

20. Where was the high tower?

1. ....

2. ....

3. ....

4. ....

5. ....

6. ....

7. ....

8. ....

9. ....

10. ....

11. ....

12. ....

13. ....

14. ....

15. ....

16. ....

17. ....

18. ....

19. ....

20. ....

Answers on page 231

ZONE ⑨

MEMORY TEST 5

Study the school timetable on the next page for 3 minutes, then begin the test on the following page.

ONCE THE TEST HAS STARTED YOU
MUST NOT LOOK BACK

Set the clock and begin

Time allowed for this test
10 MINUTES

King Edward VI High School
Spring timetable

Time	Monday	Tuesday	Wednesday	Thursday	Friday
9.00 – 10.30 am	Math	English Literature	French	Math	Biology
15 min break					
10.45 – 12.30 pm	English Literature	French	English Literature	Study Period	English Literature
Lunch	Lunch	Lunch	Lunch	Lunch	Lunch
2.00 – 3.00 pm	Study Period	Economics	Biology	Geography	Math
15 min break					
3.15 – 4.30pm	Geography	Math	English Literature	English Language	Geography

1. What is the name of the school?

2. Is it the Summer term or Spring term timetable?

3. What time does Lunch start?

4. What time does Lunch end?

5. How many 15-minute breaks are there in a week?

6. What time does the day end?

7. Which two days of the week have Study Period?

8. What is the first lecture on Tuesday morning?

9. What is the last lecture on Friday afternoon?

10. What lecture is Math followed by on Monday morning?

11. How many lectures of Biology are there in the week?

12. What time does the lecture before Lunch begin?

13. What are your lectures on Monday and in what order?

14. How many lectures of Geography are there on Monday and Tuesday?

15. Does English Literature or English Language follow Geography on Thursday afternoon?

16. What time does your Math lecture begin on Friday?

17. Do you have Math on Thursday?

18. What lectures do you have on Friday morning?

19. What time does your first lecture end?

20. Do you have a French lecture on Thursday?

MORE MEMORY TESTS

1. ....

2. ....

3. ....

4. ....

5. ....

6. ....

7. ....

8. ....

9. ....

10. ....

11. ....

12. ....

13. ....

14. ....

15. ....

16. ....

17. ....

18. ....

19. ....

20. ....

Answers on page 232

MORE MEMORY TESTS

MEMORY TEST 6

Study the display of cards on the next page for 2 minutes, then begin the test on the following page.

ONCE THE TEST HAS STARTED YOU
MUST NOT LOOK BACK

Set the clock and begin

Time allowed for this test
10 MINUTES

1. How many cards are there in the first column?

2. How many cards are there altogether?

3. How many cards are there in the fourth column?

4. How many cards are there with Queen on?

5. In which column would you find the 9 of Diamonds?

6. In which column would you find the 10 of Diamonds?

7. What card is below the 4 of Hearts?

8. Which card is above the Jack of Diamonds?

9. What is the last card on the fourth column?

10. Which card is above the Ace of Hearts?

11. Are there 7 or 8 cards in the third column?

12. How many Club cards are there altogether?

13. How many Diamond cards are there altogether?

14. How many cards are there with the 10 of Hearts on?

15. In which column would you find the 3 of Diamonds?

16. Would you find the Ace of Hearts in the second or third column?

17. How many King cards are there?

18. What is the fifth card of the 2nd column?

19. What is the first card of the first column?

20. Is the 3 of Spades the last card on the 2nd column?

1. _____

2. _____

3. _____

4. _____

5. _____

6. _____

7. _____

8. _____

9. _____

10. _____

11. _____

12. _____

13. _____

14. _____

15. _____

16. _____

17. _____

18. _____

19. _____

20. _____

Answers on page 232

MORE MEMORY TESTS

MEMORY TEST 7

Study the travel agent's window display on the next page for 2 minutes, then begin the test on the following page.

ONCE THE TEST HAS STARTED YOU
MUST NOT LOOK BACK

Set the clock and begin

Time allowed for this test
10 MINUTES

KOS 14 nts
Full board $310
2nd June

BARGAIN OF THE WEEK!

LONDON WEEKEND
Great Palace Hotel
3 nts full board $350

ZANTE 14 nts
Half-board $229
15th July

ORLANDO 14 nts
Room only $449
13th June

SYDNEY 21 nts
All inclusive $2010
10th June

MAJORCA 7 nts
Full Board $159
8th June

FLIGHT DISCOUNTS

10% OFF	AMSTERDAM
10% OFF	PARIS
25% OFF	PALMA
15% OFF	BENIDORM
10% OFF	SAN FRANCISCO
10% OFF	SYDNEY
20% OFF	DELHI
25% OFF	ALGARVE
15% OFF	NICE

FRANKFURT 14 nts
Self-catering $1000
16th June

TENERIFE 14 nts
Full Board $449
15th December

1. How many flight discounts were there?

2. What was the destination of the Bargain of the Week?

3. What was the name of the Hotel of the London Weekend?

4. How much was the holiday to Orlando?

5. Was the holiday to Frankfurt Room Only or Self-Catering?

6. How much was the flight discount to Amsterdam?

7. How many holidays were there altogether?

8. Which was the cheapest holiday?

9. If you wanted to go on holiday on 15th July where would you be going?

10. Can you name the four full board holidays?

11. How many nights was the London weekend for?

12. Was the London weekend $320 or $350?

13. Which two holidays would cost you $449?

14. Where would you be going on 16th June for $1000?

15. How many 14-night holidays were available?

16. How much was off the flight to Delhi?

17. Which two flights had 25% off?

18. Which two flights had 15% off?

19. How much was off the flight to Nice?

20. How much was the holiday to Frankfurt?

1. _____

2. _____

3. _____

4. _____

5. _____

6. _____

7. _____

8. _____

9. _____

10. _____

11. _____

12. _____

13. _____

14. _____

15. _____

16. _____

17. _____

18. _____

19. _____

20. _____

Answers on page 233

ANSWERS

Memory Test 1

1. 3.
2. Bicycle.
3. 1.
4. Bottom corners.
5. Wine glass and bulb.
6. L and G.
7. 25.
8. A chair.
9. Hockey.
10. To the left of the page.
11. None.
12. Down.
13. 2.
14. Football player.
15. 4, 2.
16. 7, 3, sportscar, train.
17. A bulb.
18. 20.
19. A pencil.
20. Motorbike and rider.
21. A telephone.
22. A hammer.
23. C4.
24. D and K.
25. A bus.
26. To the right.
27. D is the fourth letter of the alphabet.
28. G.
29. O.
30. A pair of skis.

Memory Test 2

1. Indian, English, French, Italian.
2. 4.
3. 2.
4. 6000 Lire.
5. No.
6. £6.00.
7. Lamb Bhuna.
8. 2.
9. The same.
10. International Menu.
11. Indian.
12. Italian and English.
13. No.
14. 30 Francs.
15. £4.00.
16. 3.
17. Yes.
18. Credit cards are not accepted.
19. Ice Cream, Zabaglione.
20. 3.
21. Tomato and Cock-a-Leekie.
22. Shish Kebab, 900 Rupee.
23. French.
24. 100 Francs.
25. 5.
26. Minestrone Soup.
27. French.
28. £6.00.
29. 9600 Lire.
30. There was no coffee.

Memory Test 3

1. 3.
2. Saturday 19th July 1996.
3. 6.
4. 1.
5. 6.00.
6. 8.05.
7. 8.
8. *Sommersby.*
9. 2.
10. 6.35.
11. *Sports Update.*
12. 7.00.
13. 11.45.
14. Channel 3.
15. 11.45.
16. 7.45.
17. No.
18. 5.
19. 9.00.
20. 9.50.

Memory Test 4

1. 4.
2. West.
3. "The Sun descending in the west."
4. They are silent.
5. A flower.
6. Lambs.
7. The feet.
8. Wolves and tygers.
9. "New worlds to inherit."
10. Warm.
11. Their bed.
12. Thirst.
13. The sheep.
14. New worlds.
15. Happy groves.
16. 5.
17. Evening Star.
18. William Blake.
19. Night.
20. Heaven.

Memory Test 5

1. King Edward VI High School.
2. Spring Term.
3. 12.30.
4. 2.00 pm.
5. 10.
6. 4.30 pm.
7. Monday and Thursday.
8. English Literature.
9. Geography.
10. English Literature.
11. 2.
12. 10.45 am.
13. Math, English Literature, Study Period, Geography.
14. 1.
15. English Language.
16. 2.00 pm.
17. Yes.
18. Biology and English Literature.
19. 10.30 am.
20. No.

Memory Test 6

1. 6.
2. 26.
3. 6.
4. 1.
5. 4th.
6. 3rd.
7. 9 of Spades.
8. Queen of Hearts.
9. 7 of Hearts.
10. 4 of Spades.
11. 7.
12. 1.
13. 6.
14. 2.
15. 2nd.
16. 2nd.
17. 2.
18. King of Spades.
19. 8 of Diamonds.
20. Yes.

Memory Test 7

1. 9.
2. Kos.
3. Great Palace Hotel.
4. $449.
5. Self-Catering.
6. 10%.
7. 8.
8. Majorca, $159.
9. Zante.
10. Kos, Majorca, Tenerife, London.
11. 3 nights.
12. $350.
13. Orlando, Tenerife.
14. Frankfurt.
15. 5.
16. 20%.
17. Palma, Algarve.
18. Benidorm, Nice.
19. 15%.
20. $1000.

SCORING SYSTEM

Has the Mind Assault Course damaged your memory?

Promotion Criteria (See page 21):

Average Score per test

Less than 6 :	*"Suggest a new trade."* Demoted one rank.
7 – 10	No progress.
11 – 14	Promoted one rank.
15 +	Promoted two ranks and selected for Special Forces.

AGE BONUS POINTS

AGE IN YEARS	10	10.5	11	11.5	12	12.5	13	13.5	14	14.5	15	15.5
BONUS POINTS	3	3	3	3	2	2	2	2	1	1	1	0

234

ZONE ⑩

> **Struggle through this final test of endurance using your logic and visual awareness and you could be considered fit for service in the Mensa Special Forces.**

THE FINAL ASSAULT

OBSTACLE 1   Which of the following is the odd one out?

1.

A   **B**   **C**   **D**   **E**

2.

      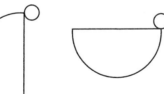      

A   **B**   **C**   **D**   **E**

Answers on page 254

3.

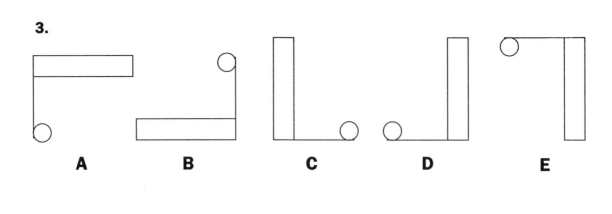

A **B** **C** **D** **E**

4.

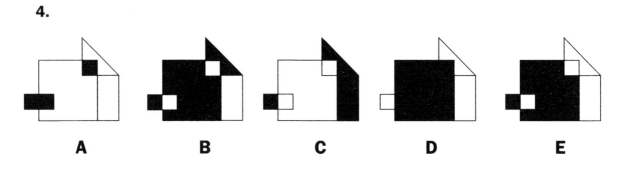

A **B** **C** **D** **E**

5.

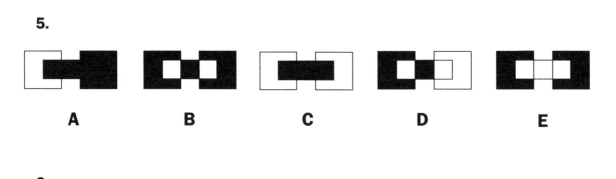

A **B** **C** **D** **E**

6.

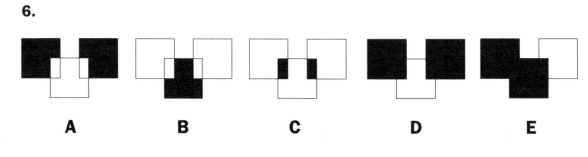

A **B** **C** **D** **E**

Answers on page 254

7.

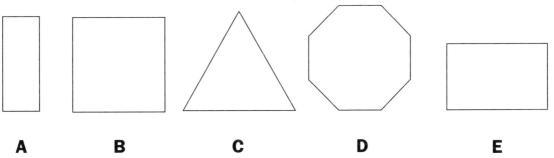

A **B** **C** **D** **E**

8.

A **B** **C** **D** **E**

9.

A **B** **C** **D** **E**

THE FINAL ASSAULT

Answers on page 254

10.

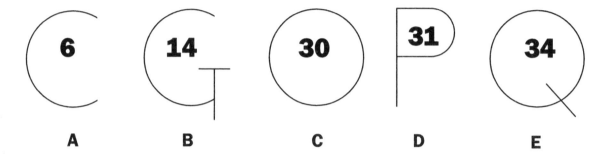

A   **B**   **C**   **D**   **E**

OBSTACLE 2   Should A, B, C, or D fill the empty circle?

11.

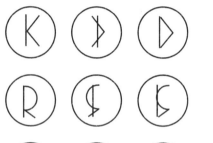

A   **B**   **C**   **D**

12.

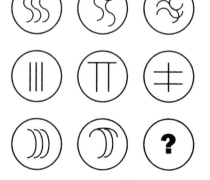

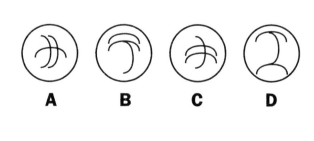

A   **B**   **C**   **D**

13.

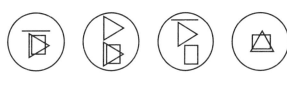

A   B   C   D

14.

A   B   C   D

15.

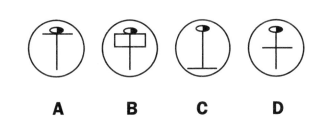

A   B   C   D

THE FINAL ASSAULT

OBSTACLE 3 No symbol is used on more than one side of the box. Which of these is not a view of the same box?

16.

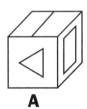   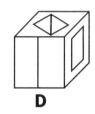 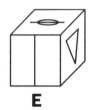 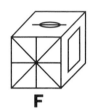

A   B   C   D   E   F

17.

 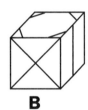 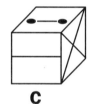  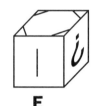 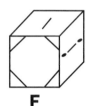

A   B   C   D   E   F

18.

A   B   C   D   E   F

19.

A   B   C   D   E   F

20.

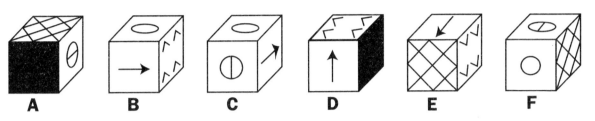

OBSTACLE 4 Which of these boxes can be made from the template? Is it A, B, C, D, E, or F? No sign is repeated on more than one side of the box.

21.

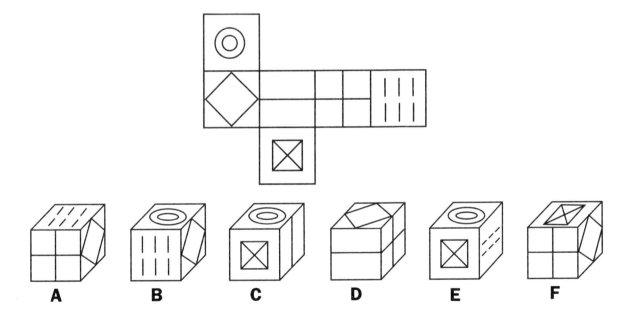

Answers on page 255

241

22.

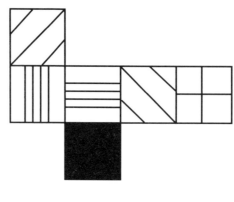

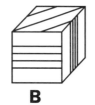   

A   B   C   D   E   F

23.

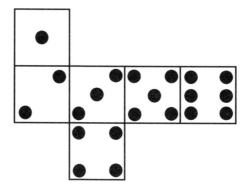

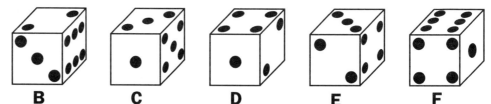

A   B   C   D   E   F

Answers on page 255

24.

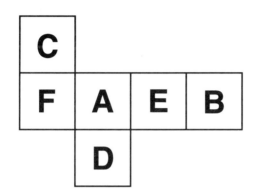

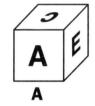
A

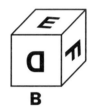
B

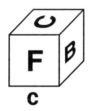
C

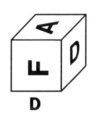
D

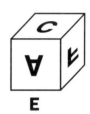
E

F

25.

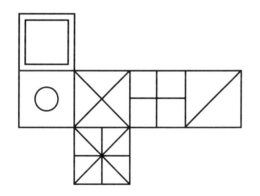

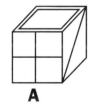
A

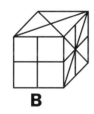
B

C

D

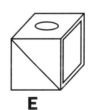
E

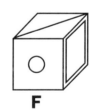
F

Answers on page 255

THE FINAL ASSAULT

OBSTACLE 5 These are all mirror image problems. One of the 4 given images has an error on it.

A 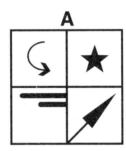 **B** 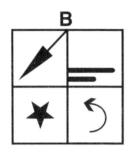 **C**  **D**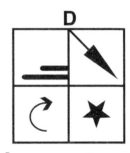

Rearranged

A **C**

D **B**

B is the odd one out as  should be

26.

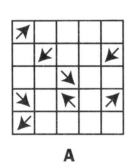 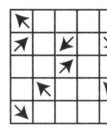 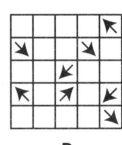

A **B** **C** **D**

27.

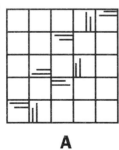 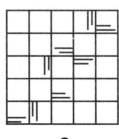 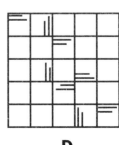

A **B** **C** **D**

Answer on page 255

28.

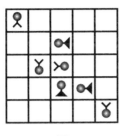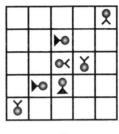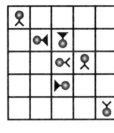

A   B   C   D

29.

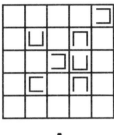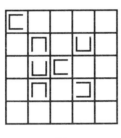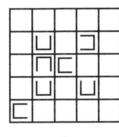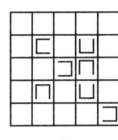

A   B   C   D

30.

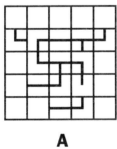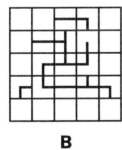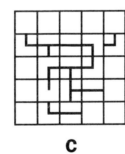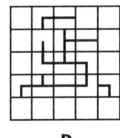

A   B   C   D

Answers on page 255

THE FINAL ASSAULT

OBSTACLE 6

31.

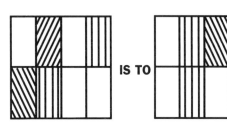 IS TO 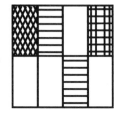 AS IS TO **?**

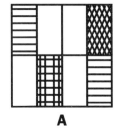

A   B   C   D

32.

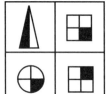 IS TO 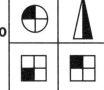 AS 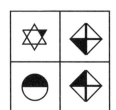 IS TO **?**

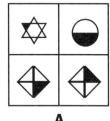

A   B   C   D

(**Answers on page 255**)

33.

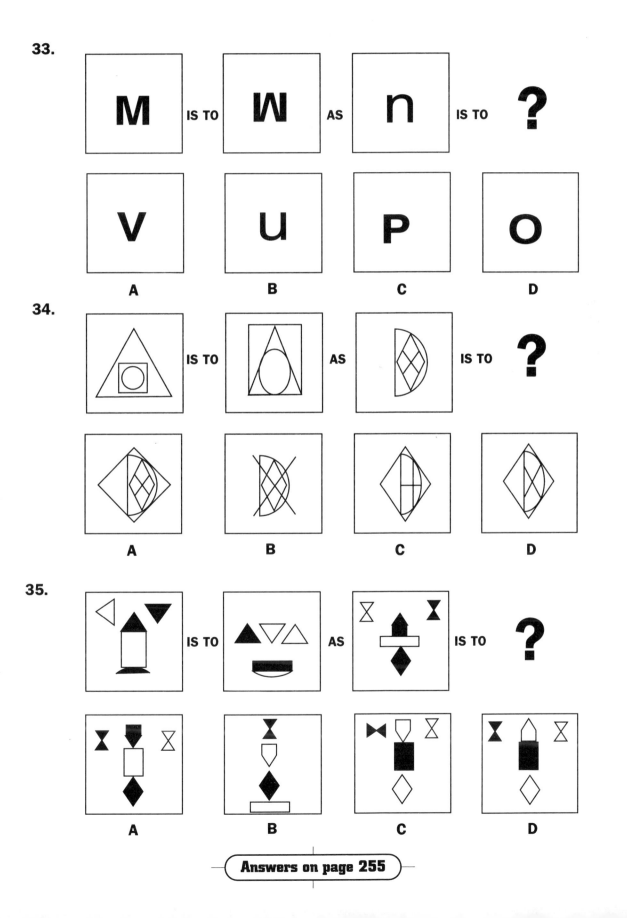

34.

35.

THE FINAL ASSAULT

OBSTACLE 7 Which of the shapes, A, B, C, D, or E cannot be made from the dots if a line is drawn through all of the dots at least once?

36.

  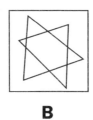 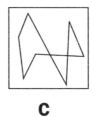 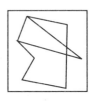 

A   B   C   D   E

37.

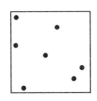 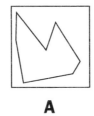 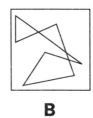   

A   B   C   D   E

38.

 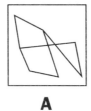  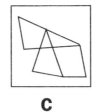  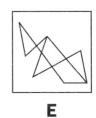

A   B   C   D   E

39.

   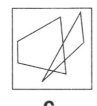 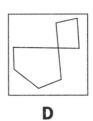 

A   B   C   D   E

40.

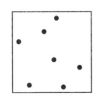    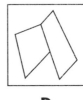 

A   B   C   D   E

(Answers on page 255)

OBSTACLE 8   Should A, B, C, or D come next in this series?

41.

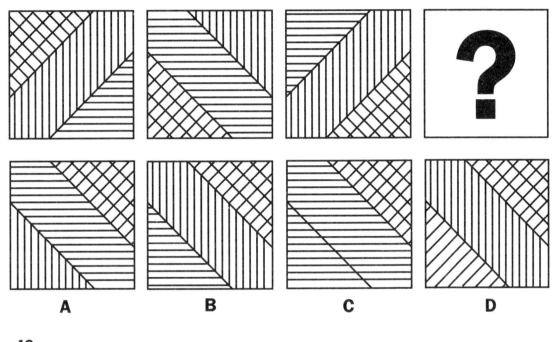

42.

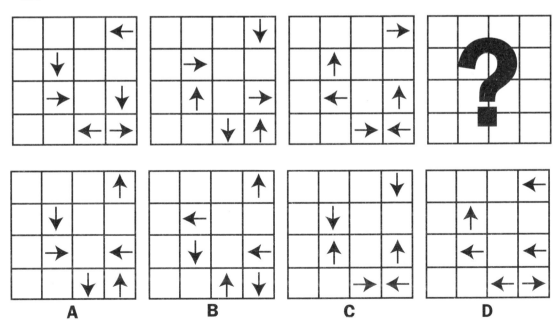

43.

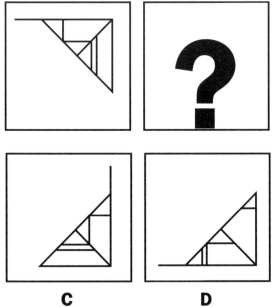

| A | B | C | D |

44.

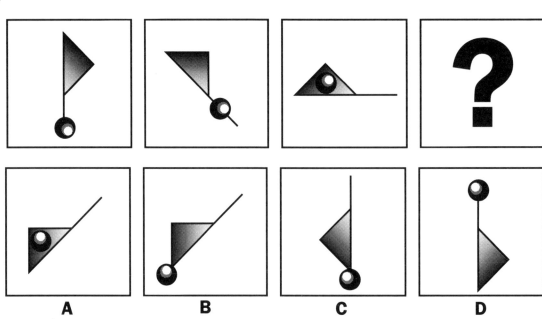

| A | B | C | D |

THE FINAL ASSAULT

45.

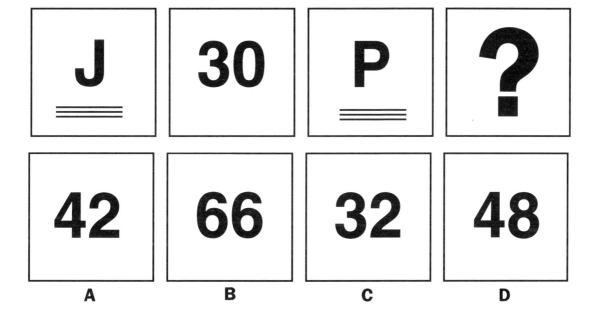

46.

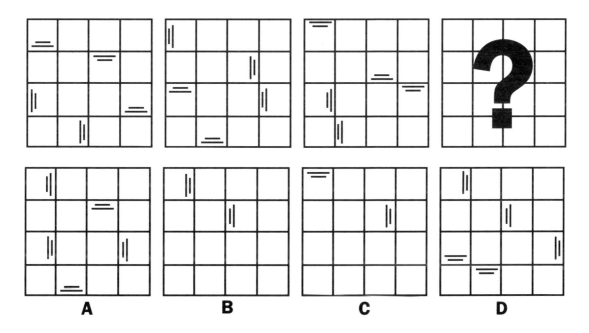

Answers on page 256

THE FINAL ASSAULT

47.

HB28	DC34	GA17	?

EI95	EI90	EI85	EI100
A	B	C	D

48.

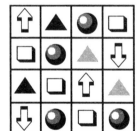 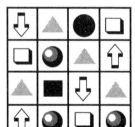 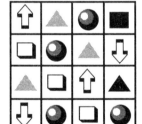 

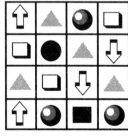 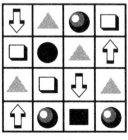 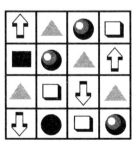 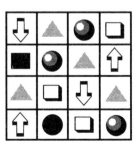

A   B   C   D

49.

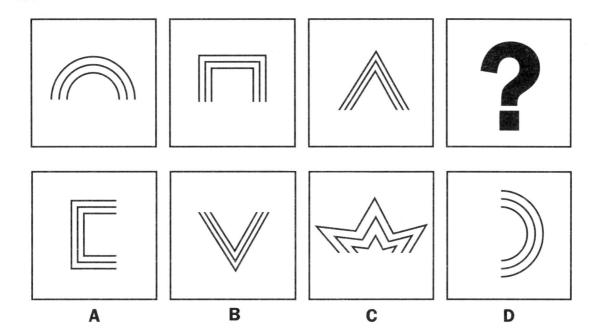

50.

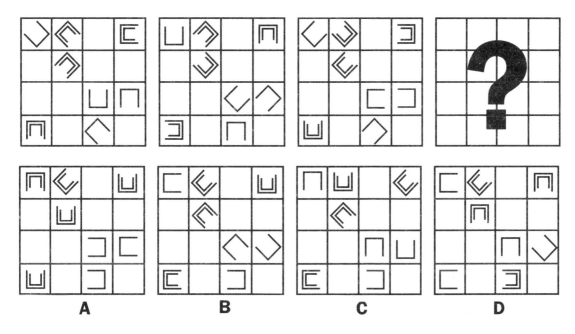

THE FINAL ASSAULT

ANSWERS

OBSTACLE 1

1. C. Others are matched opposite pairs.
2. B. Others rotate into each other.
3. D. Others rotate into each other.
4. E. Has only two segments shaded; the others have three.
5. E. Only one with middle square white.
6. E. Not symmetrical around a vertical middle.
7. D. Others have six lines.
8. A. Others rotate into each other.
9. C. Not symmetrical around horizontal axis.
10. D. Number denotes twice the alphabetical position.

OBSTACLE 2

11. D. Letter reverses, stick moves to the left.
12. C. One vertical line moves to a horizontal position, then two lines move to a horizontal position.
13. B. First letter contains two straight lines, second letter contains three straight lines, and third letter contains four straight lines.
14. B. Vertical object moves 45° clockwise, then a further 45° clockwise, then doubles.
15. C. Horizontal object moves down, small shape moves down then up again.

OBSTACLE 3

16.	A.		**17.**	B.
18.	D.		**19.**	D.
20.	E.			

OBSTACLE 4

21.	B.		**22.**	C.
23.	E.		**24.**	D.
25.	A.			

OBSTACLE 5

26. B.
27. D.
28. D.
29. C.
30. A.

OBSTACLE 6

31. A. Move sections three places clockwise.
32. C. Boxes rotate clockwise and opposite segments are shaded.
33. B. Same upside-down.
34. D. Shapes get longer and outside shape moves.
35. C. White shapes turn 90° clockwise. Black shapes turn 180°. Black becomes white and white becomes black.

OBSTACLE 7

36.	E.		**37.**	C.
38.	D.		**39.**	E.
40.	A.			

THE FINAL ASSAULT

Answers

THE FINAL ASSAULT

OBSTACLE 8

41. A. Box rotates 90° anti- (counter) clockwise.
42. B. Each segment rotates 90° anti- (counter) clockwise.
43. C. Turns 90° clockwise.
44. B. Turns 45° anti- (counter) clockwise, circle moves along.
45. D. Alpha position multiplied by the number of lines.
46. D. Short and long lines swap places and rotate clockwise.
47. A. Alpha values reversed.
48. D. Arrows reverse direction. Shading moves one place.
49. C. Lines point down.
50. B. Each shape moves clockwise, 45° with one line, 90° with two.

SCORING SYSTEM

Your destiny depends on the results of this test.

Promotion Criteria (See page 21):

Under 20	Busted one rank.
21 – 30	No promotion.
31 – 40	Promoted one rank.
41 +	Promoted two ranks.

AGE BONUS CHART

AGE IN YEARS	10	10.5	11	11.5	12	12.5	13	13.5	14	14.5	15	15.5
BONUS POINTS	10	10	8	8	7	6	6	5	4	3	2	1